Foundations for Algebra: Year 1

Managing Editors:

Elizabeth Coyner
  Bear River School
Beverly Brockhoff
  Glen Edwards Middle School

Small $1.00   Medium   Large

Illustrator:

Jonathan Weast
    Weast & Weast Illustration Studio
    Sacramento, California

Technical Assistance:

Bethany Sorbello
    CPM Educational Program
Thu Pham
    The CRESS Center
    University of California, Davis

Developed by CPM Educational Program

Program Directors:

Judith Kysh
    Departments of Mathematics and Education
    San Francisco State University
Tom Sallee
    Department of Mathematics
    University of California, Davis
Brian Hoey
    CPM Educational Program

v 3.0

Credits for the First Edition

Substantially Revised (2000, 2001)
by

Heidi Ackley
Steve Ackley
Elizabeth Baker
Bev Brockhoff
Ellen Cafferata
Elizabeth Coyner
Sara Effenbeck
William Funkhouser
Brian Hoey
Carol Jancsi

Judy Kysh
Kris Petersen
Robert Petersen
Edwin Reed
Stacy Rocklein
Kristie Sallee
Tom Sallee
Howard Webb
Kaye Whitney
Jon Wickham

Pilot Edition Contributing Editors (1999)

Heidi Ackley
Steve Ackley
Bev Brockhoff
Ellen Cafferata
Elizabeth Coyner
Scott Coyner
Kathleen Davies
Merci Del Rosario
Virginia Downing
Sara Effenbeck
Alice Elstien
William Ford

William Funkhouser
Bruce Grip
Stephen Inouye
Carol Jancsi
Alvin Mendle, Jr.
Pattie Montgomery
Edwin Reed
Gail Standiford
Gale Sunderland
Howard Webb
Kaye Whitney
Jon Wickham

Technical Assistance

Jennifer Buddenhagen
Grace Chen
Ankit Jain
Janelle Petersen

Jeremy Tauzer
David Trombly
Erika Wallender
Emily Wheelis

4 5 6 7 8 9 10 11 12   05 04   **VERSION 3.0**

Printed in the United States of America   ISBN 1-931287-01-5

Foundations for Algebra: Year 1
First Edition
Table of Contents

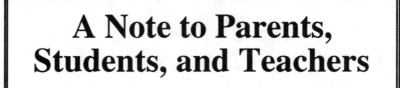

A Note to Parents, Students, and Teachers

Welcome to *Foundations for Algebra: Year 1.*

This textbook will prepare students for future Algebra courses. It was also written to consolidate the core ideas of previous mathematics courses, so that it will serve students of varied mathematics backgrounds. The contents of this course are many of the fundamental ideas and procedures necessary to be successful in subsequent mathematics courses and many careers. Classroom teachers wrote the lessons to present these ideas in ways that have proven successful with their students. The course also meets local, state, and national curriculum standards.

The investigations, problems, and practice exercises are designed to develop the students' logical and mathematical reasoning skills. The sequence of problems leads to understanding the reasoning behind the mathematical concepts. Students complete guided investigations that explore and develop ideas, then practice them along with procedural skills in subsequent chapters. Many problems use the mathematics in situations like those encountered by students and adults in their daily activities and business settings.

In order to be successful in mathematics it is critical that students actively participate in their learning. This means that each student must read and work all of the problems. Students need to discuss mathematical concepts and the reasoning involved in the steps of their solutions. In order to provide these discussion opportunities, students are encouraged to work with a study partner and in study teams both inside and outside the classroom. It is critical that students complete ALL of the assignments, including homework, to develop their individual skills. Equally important is that students take accurate, complete notes and ask questions about any problem, question, or concept that they find confusing or difficult to understand.

There are two additional resources that the authors designed to help students be successful in this course. The first is the mathematics Tool Kit that contains most of the ideas a student needs to know in the course. Tool Kit entries appear in the student text and in a Tool Kit booklet. The other is the *Foundations for Algebra Parent Guide.* The guide is sometimes available from the classroom teacher or the school library. It is available through the Internet at www.cpm.org. It may also be purchased directly from CPM Educational Program for $20 plus $3 shipping (California residents please add local sales tax to the $20) by sending a check to CPM, 1233 Noonan Drive, Sacramento, CA 95822.

Chapter 1

Chapter 1
Algebra Rocks! **INTEGERS and DATA INTERPRETATION**

Data is all around us! Successful people analyze and interpret hundreds or even thousands of pieces of information every day. In this course you will learn several ways to organize data effectively. In this chapter you will:

- find sums with positive and negative integers.

- determine which number(s) makes an equation true.

- scale the axes of graphs.

- determine the measures of central tendency (mode, median, mean) for a set of data.

- display data in a stem-and-leaf plot.

- summarize the main ideas from the chapter.

Read the problem below, but **do not try to solve it now**. What you learn over the next few days will enable you to solve it.

AR-0.   Numbers can be quite persuasive in helping you convince someone that what you claim to be true is in fact true. Collecting and organizing data, often gathered from surveys, is one important skill you need to make sense of data. By the end of this chapter, you will know some of the standard methods for analyzing and displaying data sets.

Number Sense

Algebra and Functions

Mathematical Reasoning

Measurement and Geometry

Statistics, Data Analysis, & Probability

Chapter 1
Algebra Rocks! INTEGERS and DATA INTERPRETATION

AR-1. You will be working in pairs or teams of four. You need to be able to work cooperatively with many different people whether in school or on a job. Working as a team is a valuable skill. Today you will interview your partner. Follow your teacher's directions. Then you will introduce your partner to another pair.

- What is your name?

- What other states or countries have you visited?

- How far from school do you live? How do you get to school?

- What is your favorite school subject?

- What career would you like to have when you are out of school, that is, after high school or college?

AR-2. Hamida and her cousin were helping their grandfather tile a floor. When he left to get more supplies, they decided to invent a new game. They called it "Some Sum." They wanted to see who could grab the biggest sum of tile spacers in one handful. Each of them took a handful of spacers and counted them out.

Sayed: How many did you get?

Hamida: I got eleven.

Sayed: I have twelve. That means I win!

Hamida: Not so fast! They aren't all the same shape. Some of them look like plus signs and the others are straight.

Sayed: The straight spacers look like minus signs. Let's pair each plus with a minus. Our score will come from our remaining tiles. I have six of the straight ones and six of the ones that look like plus signs.

Hamida: I have six plusses too, but I only have five straight ones.

a) Sketch a picture of Sayed's tile spacers.

b) Sketch a picture of Hamida's tile spacers.

c) Now it is time for you and your teammate to decide who won. Explain your decision using complete sentences. Be ready to share your decision and convince your classmates that your choice is correct.

AR-3.   Now it is your turn to play Some Sum. Gently take a handful of tile spacers.

   a)   Determine your score. Represent your tile spacers with a picture.

   b)   Sketch a picture of your teammate's handful and score.

   c)   Who won?

   d)   Is there a quick way to determine the winner when someone has a huge handful?

AR-4.   **Algebra Puzzles** Algebra puzzles will appear throughout this book. They give you a
         new way to apply the number skills you have already learned. Here is the first one.

         Decide which number belongs in the blank to make the equation true. If you cannot find
         the answer just by looking, try several different numbers until you find the answer.
         Notice the dot in each part of this problem. The dot means that you multiply the first
         number by the number that goes in the blank that follows it. You have used an x for
         multiplication in the past. You will no longer do so. For now you should use the dot or
         parentheses for multiplication. If you continue to use x for multiplication, you could
         confuse it with the letters used in algebra.

   a) $3 \cdot \underline{} + 2 = 14$ b) $4 \cdot \underline{} + 1 = 21$

   c) $6 \cdot \underline{} + 7 = 25$ d) $5 \cdot \underline{} - 3 = 42$

AR-5.
         Many students have difficulty taking notes for a math
         class, so we will make some suggestions to assist you
         with this study skill. You will keep all of your math
         notes together in a special place called a Tool Kit.

         When it is time to make notes, a Tool Kit icon like the
         one at left will be printed in the textbook under the
         problem number. The information about which you
         will make notes will appear inside a double-lined box.
         The double-lined box will be printed in two places: in
         the textbook and in your Tool Kit. Some schools use
         the bound Tool Kit from CPM; others photocopy the
         pages and have you put them in a three-ring binder.

         Sometimes you will write keywords, a phrase, or a list. Other times you will need to
         write one or more complete sentences. Next to the double-lined box in your Tool Kit is a
         place for you to make notes. Follow the directions below each Tool Kit problem in the
         textbook and write neatly so that your notes will be useful.

>>Problem continues on the next page.>>

This is your first Tool Kit notation.

STUDY TEAM GUIDELINES

1. **Each member of the team is responsible for his or her own behavior.**

Make these notes in your Tool Kit to the right of the double-lined box.

a) Highlight the words "responsible," "own," and "behavior."

b) List some behaviors of a student who is following this guideline.

c) List some behaviors of a student who is not following this guideline.

AR-6.   Organization is a key component of success in almost everything you do. You will need to keep an organized binder for this course. Follow the guidelines set by your teacher.

- You will need a sturdy three-ring binder with a hard cover.

- Put your name on the inside front cover of this binder.

- Divide your binder into labeled sections as directed by your teacher.

After you have completed this task, write, "I have organized my binder" next to the problem number in your notebook.

AR-7.   Compute the answer to each of the following expressions and explain your steps.

a) $2 + 3 + 4 + 5$ b) $2 + 3 + 4 - 5$

c) $2 - 3 - 4 + 5$ d) $2 + 3 - 4 - 5$

AR-8. **Mathography** A mathography is a lot like your life history, except that it is focused on mathematics in your life

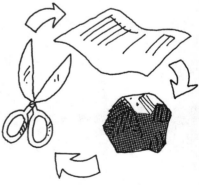

a) On a separate piece of paper, write a letter about yourself to your teacher. The letter will help your teacher get to know you as an individual. The letter should address these three general topics: you, you as a student, and you as a math student. Remember to use complete sentences and make sure your work is neat enough to be easily read. Start the letter with "Dear ..." Make sure you sign your letter. This should take about fifteen minutes to complete. Parts (b), (c), and (d) have suggestions for each of the three topics.

b) **You**: Introduce yourself, using the name you like to be called. What languages do you speak? Describe your hobbies, talents, and interests. State your goals or dreams. What are you proud of? What else would you like to share?

c) **You as a Student**: Describe the importance of school in your life. Describe yourself as a student. In what kinds of classroom activities do you excel? What kinds of activities do you find frustrating? Explain which subject(s) is/are your favorite(s). Tell why you like it (them). How regularly do you finish in-class assignments? How faithfully do you do your homework?

d) **You as a Math Student**: Describe your most memorable moment in math and explain why you remember it. State your favorite math topic. Name your least favorite. Explain how you feel about math this year. What grade do you expect to earn in this class?

AR-9. Parveen and Sharin were playing Some Sum. Determine the value of each of the handfuls of tiles shown below. Draw an organized picture next to your answer.

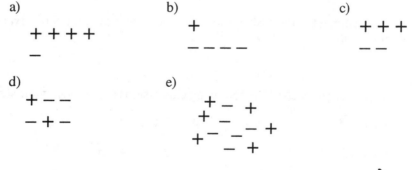

a)

$$+ + + +$$
$$-$$

b)

$$+$$
$$- - - -$$

c)

$$+ + +$$
$$- -$$

d)

$$+ - -$$
$$- + -$$

e)

$$+ - +$$
$$+ - $$
$$+ - - +$$
$$- +$$

AR-10. **Rock-Paper-Scissors** Use the instructions below to play Rock-Paper-Scissors with a partner. Playing the game gives you practice combining positives (+) and negatives (–), a skill you need for adding positive and negative numbers.

>>Problem continues on the next page.>>

CHAPTER 1

Rock-Paper-Scissors
A game for two people.

Mathematical Purpose: To practice adding integers.

Object: To have the most points at the end of five rounds.

Materials: Tile spacers and paper to record the scores.

Scoring: The winner of a round gets plus tiles and the opponent gets minus tiles in the amounts shown in the table below.

Rock wins +++	Scissors lose −
Paper wins ++	Rock loses − − −
Scissors win +	Paper loses − −

How to Play the Game:
- At the same time as your teammate, shake your fist three times and then display either a closed fist for "rock," a flat hand for "paper," or a partly closed fist with two extended fingers for "scissors."
- Rock beats Scissors (because rock blunts scissors), Scissors beat Paper (because scissors cut paper), and Paper beats Rock (because paper can wrap-up a rock). If you tie, repeat the round.
- Record your points on a table like the one below.
- Play a total of five rounds, not including ties.

Round	(Your Name)	(Your Partner's Name)
1		
2		
3		
4		
5		
Total		

Ending the Game: When you have completed five rounds, the person with the highest sum of tile spacers is the winner.

a) How many rounds did you win?

b) How many rounds did your partner win?

c) What was your final score?

d) What was your partner's final score?

e) Who won the game (five rounds)?

f) Did the person who won the greatest number of rounds also win the game?

AR-11.   **Algebra Puzzles** Decide which number belongs in the blank to make the equation true. If you cannot find the answer just by looking, start by trying 10 and then try larger or smaller numbers.

a) $2 \cdot \underline{} - 5 = 17$ b) $4 \cdot \underline{} - 1 = 51$

c) $7 \cdot \underline{} - 4 = 59$ d) $5 \cdot \underline{} - 3 = 72$

AR-12.

STUDY TEAM GUIDELINES

1. Each member of the team is responsible for his or her own behavior.

2. **Each member of the team must be willing to help any other team member who asks for help.**

In your Tool Kit, highlight the words "each member" and "willing to help."

AR-13.   **Multiplication Timed Test I**

Use the resource page provided by your teacher to complete the first timed multiplication test. You have five minutes to fill in as many of the answers as you can. When you finish, write, "I took Multiplication Timed Test I" next to this problem number in your notebook.

AR-14.   Once you have corrected the multiplication test, answer each question below.

a)   How many problems were on this test?

b)   How many problems did you complete in the five minutes?

c)   How many problems did you answer correctly?

d)   What percent of the problems did you complete? (Percent means "out of 100.")

e)   What percent of the 100 problems did you answer correctly?

Later you will take more timed multiplication tests. Practice multiplication at home to improve your speed.

AR-15.   Going forward 5 steps can be undone by going backward 5 steps. Find a way to undo each of the actions below.

a)   up 10 steps   b)   rise of 5 degrees   c)   earn 8 dollars

d)   loss of 6 dollars   e)   south 3 kilometers   f)   backward 9 steps

AR-16. Parveen and Sharin decided to play a game of Rock-Paper-Scissors using the spacers to keep track of their points. After playing a round, they had the following scores:

a) Who won the first round?

b) Who won the second round?

c) Who was ahead after the second round?

d) Who won the fifth round?

e) Combine all five rounds for each girl to determine who won the game.

Round	Parveen	Sharin
1	+	--
2	---	++
3	+	--
4	---	++
5	++	---

AR-17. Use this checklist to review the assignments you have completed. Fix anything you missed.

a) Is your name at the top of each piece of paper?

b) Is the date on each piece of paper?

c) Did you write the problem number in the margin next to your work for each problem?

d) Is your work written neatly enough to review easily? To be read by a teammate?

e) Are there any other items that your teacher asked you to include with your assignments? Are they included in your work so far?

AR-18. Copy the figures below, then divide and shade the shapes to represent the given fraction.

a) $\frac{1}{3}$

b) $\frac{2}{5}$

c) $\frac{3}{6}$

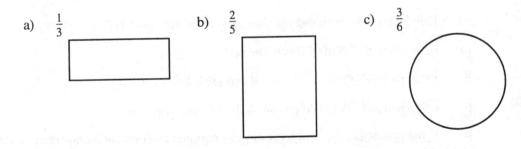

AR-19. Describe each picture by writing a sentence that includes a fraction. For example, in part (a), you could write, "$\frac{2}{5}$ of the circles are filled in." Write a different sentence for part (a) and then do parts (b) and (c).

a)

b)

c)

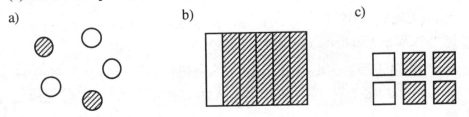

AR-20.   Your teacher will give you a problem to calculate in your head. There are several ways to do the problem. Which method do you think is best?

AR-21.   The purpose of this exercise is to develop the skill of working with others when you may not always agree with their ideas.

   a)   Working alone, list two or three of your favorites in each category.

        Soft Drinks   Movies   Sports
        Books   Food   Board Games
        Ice Cream   School Subjects

   b)   When you and your partner have completed your own lists, show them to each other. Your task now is to try to reach agreement on one item for each category as a team "favorite." Your team favorite may not necessarily be your own first choice. Write your agreed upon choice for as many categories as you can and list the ones you could not agree on. Be prepared to report on your negotiations.

AR-22.   **Multiplication Timed Test II**

   Use the resource page provided by your teacher to complete this second timed multiplication test. You have five minutes to fill in as many of the answers as you can. When you finish, write, "I took Multiplication Timed Test II" next to this problem number in your notebook.

AR-23.   Once you have corrected Multiplication Timed Test II, answer each question below.

   a)   How many problems were on this test?

   b)   How many problems did you complete in the five minutes?

   c)   How many problems did you answer correctly?

   d)   What percent of the problems did you complete?

   e)   What percent of the 100 problems did you answer correctly?

   f)   Later you will take another timed test. Do you plan to practice for it? Why or why not?

AR-24.   Mrs. Poppington's class wanted to find the average score on Multiplication Timed Test I.

   a)   What is an average?

   b)   How do you find an average?

   c)   Mrs. Poppington has eight teams in her class. The average scores for each team were 70, 60, 50, 45, 80, 75, 30, and 62. What was the class average?

AR-25. Mrs. Poppington's class wanted to see if the average had improved by the second timed multiplication test. The team scores were 85, 70, 60, 66, 72, 63, 50, and 70.

a) What is the class average? b) Had her class improved?

c) Find the average of your first two timed multiplication tests. Is your score higher or lower than the average of Multiplication Timed Test II for Mrs. Poppington's class?

d) What is the most common score of the second test in Mrs. Poppington's class?

AR-26.

┌───┐
║   **MEAN**   ║
║   ║
║ The **MEAN** is the arithmetic average of a data set. One way to determine the mean ║
║ is to add all values in a set of data and divide the sum by the number of values. ║
║   ║
║ Example: Find the mean of this set of data: 57, 44, 52, 49, and 53. ║
║   • 57 + 44 + 52 + 49 + 53 = 255   ║
║   • 255 ÷ 5 (the number of values) = 51, so the mean is 51. ║
└───┘

Make these notes in your Tool Kit to the right of the double-lined box.

a) Highlight the word "average."

b) List at least three kinds of data for which you might need to find the mean.

AR-27.

┌───┐
║   **MODE**   ║
║   ║
║ The **MODE** is the value in a data set that occurs more often than any other value. ║
║ Data sets may have more than one mode, and some do not have any mode. The mode ║
║ is useful when the data are not numeric, such as showing a "most popular" choice. ║
║   ║
║ Example: Find the mode of this set of data: 11, 13, 14, 9, 7, 15, 14, 10. ║
║   ║
║   11   13 ⑭ 9   7   15 ⑭ 10   ║
║   The mode of this data set is 14.   ║
└───┘

Highlight the phrase "occurs more often" in your Tool Kit.

AR-28.   Study the graph at right.

a)   What is the mean of the sales
      shown in the graph? Be sure
      to refer back to your Tool Kit
      if you need a reminder of
      how to calculate the mean.

b)   What is the mode for the
      daily sales?

c)   What is the highest daily
      sales figure?

d)   What is the lowest daily sales figure?

e)   What is the difference between the highest and lowest sales? (The difference
      between the highest and lowest pieces of data is called the **range**.)

$ Sales at the Student Store

(graph: Total ($) vs Day; Day 1 $30, Day 2 $30, Day 3 $20, Day 4 $20, Day 5 $10, Day 6 $40)

AR-29.   Play another game of Rock-Paper-Scissors
          with a partner and record your scores. Look
          back at problem AR-10 for the scoring rules.

a)   How many rounds did you win?

b)   How many rounds did your partner win?

c)   What was your final score?

d)   What was your partner's final score?

e)   Who won the game (five rounds)?

f)   Did the person who won the greatest number of rounds also win the game?

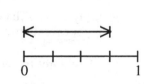

AR-30.   Represent each picture with a fraction.

a)   b)   c)

                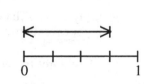

AR-31.   Represent the shaded pieces numerically in three ways: as a sum, as a product, and as a fraction. An example is shown below.

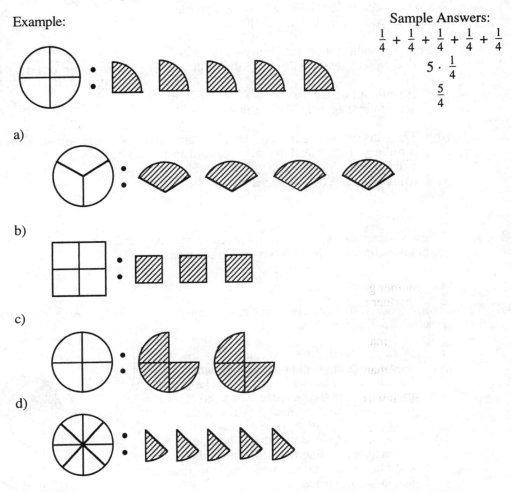

Example:

Sample Answers:

$\frac{1}{4} + \frac{1}{4} + \frac{1}{4} + \frac{1}{4} + \frac{1}{4}$

$5 \cdot \frac{1}{4}$

$\frac{5}{4}$

a)

b)

c)

d)

AR-32.   Al says that the fraction $\frac{1}{2}$ represents the picture at right. Jake disagrees and thinks it is $1\frac{1}{2}$. Martha says, "You're both right." Who is right? Explain your reasoning.

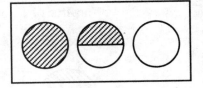

AR-33.   Pedro played 11 rounds of Rock-Paper-Scissors and got the following scores: -3, 2, 1, -1, 3, -2, -2, 1, -1, -1, and 3. Find the mean of Pedro's scores.

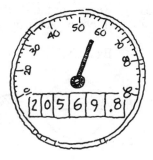

AR-34. When you see the light bulb icon below a problem number, expect the problem to challenge you.

The mileage indicator on our family's car reads 20,569.8. Note that all the digits are different.

a) How far do we have to drive before all the digits are different again? What is that number?

b) The numbers 101, 1221, and 1357531, among many others, are all **palindromic numbers**. (They read the same forward as they do backward.) How far beyond the initial odometer reading in this problem do we have to drive before the digits form a palindrome? What is that palindrome?

AR-35. Follow your teacher's directions for practicing mental math. Of the solution methods your class discussed, show the one you liked best.

AR-36. The purpose of this exercise is to get to know your study team members and to practice working together.

a) With your team draw two concentric circles on a whole sheet of paper and divide the space between the circles into as many parts as you have team members. See the example for a team of four at right. Each team member gets a section.

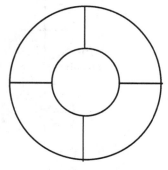

b) In the inner circle, take turns listing one characteristic you have in common with the others on your team. Characteristics might include age, height, or birthplace.

c) In the outer circle, take turns listing one characteristic about you that is unique (not true of anyone else in the team).

d) Take two or more turns in the inner and outer circles for each team member.

AR-37.

MEDIAN

The **MEDIAN** is the middle value in a set of data <u>arranged</u> in <u>numerical order</u>. If there is an even number of values, the median is the mean of the two middle values.

Example: Find the median of this set of data: 14, 103, 5, 38, 60, 6, 77, 13, 62, and 95.

- Arrange the data in order: 5, 6, 13, 14, 38, 60, 62, 77, 95, and 103.
- Find the middle value(s): 5, 6, 13, 14, (38), (60), 62, 77, 95, 103
- Where there are two middle values, find their mean:
  $38 + 60 = 98 \Rightarrow 98 \div 2 = 49$ (the median)

Note: **numerical order** means to write the numbers from smallest to largest.

Highlight the phrases "middle value," "arranged in numerical order," and "mean of the two middle values" in your Tool Kit. Then explain how to find the median of:

a) an even number of data points.   b) a non-ordered data set.

AR-38. One way to display data for further analysis is to use a **stem-and-leaf plot**. The example at right shows how to write the scores 42, 45, 56, 52, and 63 in a stem-and-leaf plot.

```
4 | 2 5
5 | 2 6
6 | 3
```

a) Notice that the leaves (the "ones" portion of the number) for 56 and 52 are in numerical order. Copy the stem-and-leaf plot shown above right and add the scores 49, 59, 57, and 67 to it.

b) Find the median of the data in the complete stem-and-leaf plot you made in part (a).

AR-39. Mrs. Poppington's class made the stem-and-leaf plot shown at right after they collected cans for a food drive. Use it to complete the parts below.

Cans collected by Mrs. Poppington's class
```
0 | 5 6
1 | 1 1 4
2 | 3 4 7
3 | 5 5 5
4 | 7 9 9
5 | 3 7
```
Key
2|3 means 23

a) List the number of cans collected by each of the students who collected 40 or more.

b) Find the mode of the data.

c) Find the median number of cans brought in by the students in Mrs. Poppington's class.

d) What do you think the key in the box above is telling you about the stems and leaves?

AR-40.   **Multiplication Timed Test III**

Use the resource page provided by your teacher to complete the third timed multiplication test. You have three minutes to fill in as many of the answers as you can. When you finish, write, "I took Multiplication Timed Test III" next to this problem number in your notebook.

AR-41.   Once you have corrected the multiplication test, answer each question below.

a)   How many problems were on this test?

b)   How many problems did you complete in the three minutes?

c)   How many problems did you answer correctly?

d)   What percent of the problems did you complete? How did you find this number?

e)   What percent of the 50 problems did you answer correctly? How did you find this number?

f)   How much did your score improve today? If it did not improve, what is your study plan?

AR-42.   What is the mean (average) for the percent correct on all three of your multiplication timed tests? If your mean is below 70%, you need to study your multiplication facts.

AR-43.   Team G in Mrs. Poppington's class took four timed multiplication tests and listed all of their scores:

           Test 1: 20, 30, 36, 34   Test 2: 40, 44, 35, 40

           Test 3: 46, 56, 48, 51   Test 4: 63, 72, 65, 72

a)   What is the mean score for the team for all four tests?

b)   Write the score for the team in order from least to greatest. Is there a "middle" score? If so, is there only one "middle" score or are there two?

c)   If you have two middle scores, how can you decide on a single number to represent the median?

d)   What number represents the median of Team G's data?

AR-44.

STEM-AND-LEAF PLOT

A **STEM-AND-LEAF PLOT** is a way to display data that shows the individual values from a set of data and how the values are distributed. The "stem" part on the graph represents the leading digit(s) of the number. The "leaf" part of the graph represents the other digit(s) of the number.

Example:

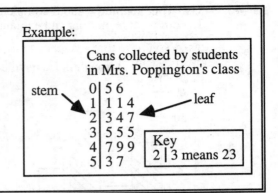

Cans collected by students in Mrs. Poppington's class

stem

0	5 6
1	1 1 4
2	3 4 7
3	5 5 5
4	7 9 9
5	3 7

leaf

Key
2 | 3 means 23

Make these notes in your Tool Kit to the right of the double-lined box.

a)   Highlight the words "stem," "represents the leading digit(s)," "leaf," and "represents the other digit(s)."

b)   From the example in the Tool Kit box, list in order the number of cans collected by each of the 16 students in Mrs. Poppington's class.

AR-45.

A COMPLETE GRAPH

Graphs are ways of displaying and comparing information. A complete data graph has the following characteristics:

• All graphs are **neat** and easy to read and, when appropriate, constructed with a **straightedge**.

• The units (or numbers) along the axes are clearly **labeled**.

• The axes (the vertical and horizontal number lines) are labeled with **words** that explain the numbers on the axes.

• The units (numbers marked on the axes) follow **equal intervals** on each axis.

• All graphs have a **title**.

• A key or **legend** is included when it is necessary to explain any symbols that are used in the graph.

Graphs should be drawn on graph paper or resource pages.

Use your highlighter to highlight any characteristics of a complete graph that you have not studied before or that you do not understand. Do this in your Tool Kit.

AR-46.   Use what you know about complete graphs to find what is missing in each graph below. Record what is missing and explain why each graph is difficult to understand.

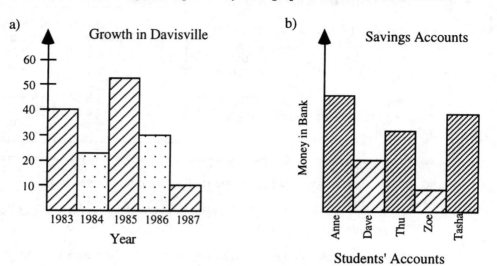

a)   Growth in Davisville

b)   Savings Accounts

c)   Daily Sales

AR-47.   Make a stem-and-leaf plot of the scores in problem AR-43 (the scores Mrs. Poppington's Team G received for all four tests).

AR-48.   **Algebra Puzzles** Decide which number belongs in the blank to make the equation true. If you cannot find the answer just by looking, try several different numbers. Work with your partner using the "pairs check" strategy outlined below.

Pairs Check:

i)   Play a game of Rock-Paper-Scissors with your partner to decide who does the first problem.

ii)   Whoever goes first explains his or her thinking while working. The other partner listens, asks questions, and helps (when asked).

iii) Then the paper and pencil go to the other partner who does part (b).

iv)   After two problems are done, each partner checks the other's work.

v)   Then take turns on parts (c) and (d) and check them.

a) $6 \cdot \underline{\quad} - 1 = 71$ b) $6 \cdot \underline{\quad} - 4 = 20$

c) $7 \cdot \underline{\quad} + 2 = 44$ d) $7 \cdot \underline{\quad} - 3 = 53$

AR-49.

STUDY TEAM GUIDELINES
1. Each member of the team is responsible for his or her own behavior.
2. Each member of the team must be willing to help any other team member who asks for help.
3. **When you have a question, ask your partner or team first. If no one can answer the question, then ask the teacher for help.**

Make these notes in your Tool Kit to the right of the double-lined box.

a)   Why do you think this is a study team guideline?

b)   Write an example of a question that most partners might be able to answer.

c)   Write an example of a question that you would need the teacher to answer.

AR-50.   **Algebra Puzzles** Decide which number belongs in the blank to make the equation true. If you cannot find the answer just by looking, try several different numbers.

a) $6 \cdot \underline{\quad} = 18$ b) $5 \cdot \underline{\quad} = 40$

c) $7 + \underline{\quad} = 12$ d) $14 - \underline{\quad} = 8$

AR-51. **Algebra Puzzles Again** These puzzles have letters in place of the blanks. Find whic number belongs in place of the letter to make the equation true. Note: A number next to variable indicates multiplication. For example, 6x means 6 times the number you use to replace the x. We refer to a letter that can be replaced by a number as a **variable**.

a) $6x = 18$ b) $5y = 40$

c) $7 + h = 12$ d) $14 - c = 8$

AR-52. Look back at the last two questions. Compare part (a) in problem AR-50 with part (a) in problem AR-51. Make the same comparison for parts (b), (c), and (d).

a)   What is the same in each pair of parts?

b)   What is different in each pair of parts?

AR-53. Five people who were all different heights lined up at the front of the room and discovered that their median height was 145 centimeters. How many people were <u>taller</u> than 145 centimeters? Explain.

AR-54.

MEASURES OF CENTRAL TENDENCY

Numbers that locate or approximate the "center" of a set of data are called **measures of central tendency**. Mean, median, and mode are measures of central tendency.

Complete the problem below in your Tool Kit to the right of the double-lined box. Be sure to check that your answers are correct with your partner or team.

A group of people were traveling together. Their ages were 11, 12, 11, 12, 38, 11, 12, 56, and 12.

a)   What is the mode of the ages?

b)   What does the mode tell you about this group of people?

c)   What is the mean age of this group?

d)   What is the median age of this group?

e)   Which measure is the best one to describe this group of people: mean, mode, or me

AR-55.   Kyia, Anthony, and Andee wanted to start their game of marbles with each of them
         having the same number of marbles. Kyia has 12, Anthony has 11, and Andee has 19.

   a)   If they all share the marbles, how many marbles should each person have to start
         the game? Explain how you found your answer. Include a sketch if it helps your
         explanation.

   b)   Briefly describe how this problem illustrates the idea of "central tendency."

AR-56.   Parveen and Sharin played a Rock-Paper-Scissors
         game as shown below.

   a)   Who won the game?

   b)   In a complete sentence, explain why.

Game	Parveen	Sharin
1	+	– –
2	– –	+
3	–	+ + +
4	+	– –
5	+ + +	–

AR-57.   Tanisha and Jorel each shaded a square to show one-half.

   a)   Tanisha's square is the one on the right, and Jorel's
         is on the left. Jorel said Tanisha did not show one-
         half correctly. Who is correct? Explain your
         reasoning.

Jorel's   Tanisha's

   b)   Wendy said she had a better way to divide a square
         in half, shown at right. Does Wendy's shaded area
         represent one-half of the square? Explain.

   c)   Harvey said, "Mine shows one-half too."
         (His square is shown at right.) Is Harvey correct?
         Explain.

AR-58.   **Algebra Puzzles**   Decide which number belongs in place of the variable to make the equation true. Note: A number next to a letter means to multiply.

a) $8m + 4 = 28$

b) $8n - 5 = 51$

c) $8h + 5 = 45$

d) $9c - 3 = 60$

AR-59.   Tony has a homework problem that he cannot solve. Can you help him? Here is the problem: There were five students of different ages whose median age was 13 years.

a)   What are two possibilities for the ages of the three older students?

b)   If each student is a different age, how many students must be younger than 13?

c)   In complete sentences, describe what a median is to another student in the class. Pretend that the student was absent the day you learned about medians.

AR-60.   Calculate the mean of each data set below.

a)   6, 10, 6, 10   b)   11, 12, 12, 13, 12   c)   -5, 5, 4, 8, 5, 7

d)   By what number did you divide in part (c) to calculate the mean?

AR-61.   Follow your teacher's directions for practicing mental math. Write down one of the solution methods different from your own.

AR-62.   Here is a number line. List two situations when you used a number line in past math classes.

AR-63. Many people use modified number lines every day. An example is the legend of a map which shows the scale for distance. Sometimes a number line is in a vertical position, that is, it has been rotated counterclockwise 90° or $\frac{1}{4}$ of a circle so the positive numbers are at the top. Decide if the items listed below are examples of number lines and write "yes" or "no" next to the item name.

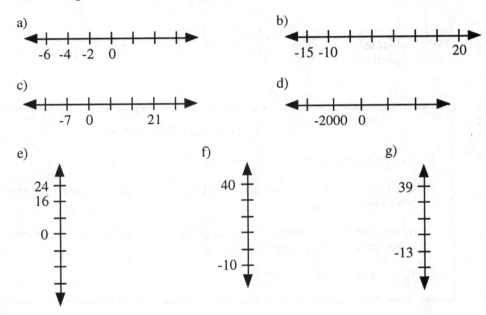

a) ruler

b) a time line

c) centimeter ruler

d) thermometer

e) elevator shaft

f) bungee cord

g) baseline on a basketball court

h) yard lines on a football field

i) yardstick

j) hiking trail through the mountains

AR-64. As you can tell from the examples of modified number lines, not all number lines increase by one unit from mark to mark. Use the resource page your teacher gives you to fill in the missing numbers on the number lines.

a)
-6 -4 -2 0

b)
-15 -10   20

c)
-7 0   21

d)
-2000 0

e)
24
16

0

f)
40

-10

g)
39

-13

AR-65.   Using the "pairs check" strategy, work with your partner to complete the scaling for each axis.

Pairs Check:

i)   Play a game of Rock-Paper-Scissors with your partner to decide who does the first problem.

ii)   Whoever goes first explains his or her thinking while working. The other partner listens, asks questions, and helps (when asked).

iii) Then the paper and pencil go to the other partner who does part (b).

iv)   After two problems are done, each partner checks the other's work.

v)   Then take turns on parts (c) and (d) and check them.

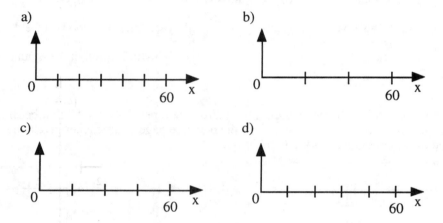

AR-66.

STUDY TEAM GUIDELINES

1. Each member of the team is responsible for his or her own behavior.

2. Each member of the team must be willing to help any other team member who asks for help.

3. When you have a question ask your partner or team first. If no one can answer the question, then ask the teacher for help.

4. **Use your team voice.**

Rewrite the fourth guideline in your own words to the right of the double-lined box in your Tool Kit.

AR-67.   Kaye just came late to class. She noticed that all the axes in problem AR-65 are numbered to 60 but that different numbers are written on each graph. Explain to her how you determined the missing numbers. Write your answer using complete sentences.

AR-68.   Sometimes a vertical number line is combined with a horizontal one to form a set of axes.
           The number lines intersect at zero. This is very similar to the axes from other graphs you
           have studied. These axes also extend in the negative direction. Use the resource page to
           scale the axes of each graph.

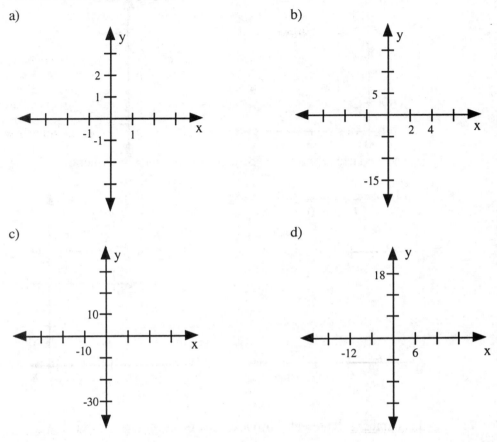

a)

b)

c)

d)

AR-69.

SCALING THE AXES OF GRAPHS

- Find the difference between the low and high numbers you need to put on the axis.
- Determine how many spaces you have on your axis.
- Divide the difference by the number of spaces on your axis to find the width of
  each space.
- Label the axis.

Example: Suppose your x-values go from -22 to 68 and you have 20 spaces. You
           need for x to increase at least $\frac{22+68}{20} = \frac{90}{20} = 4.5$ for each space. Most
           people would scale the axes by 5s.

Answer the following question in your Tool Kit to the right of the double-lined box.

How would inappropriate scaling or incorrect intervals affect a graph?

AR-70.   Complete the scales for these axes on the resource page.

a)   b)

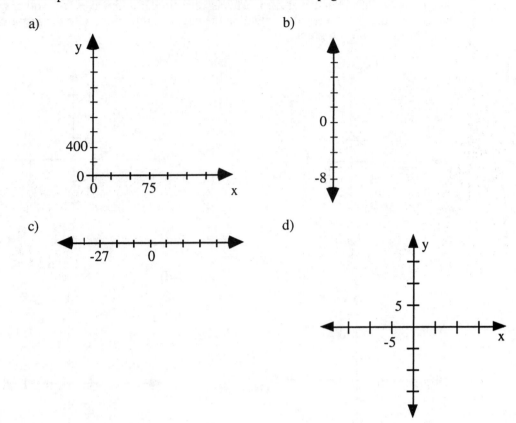

c)   d)

AR-71.   What number is represented by each letter on the number lines below?

a)   b)

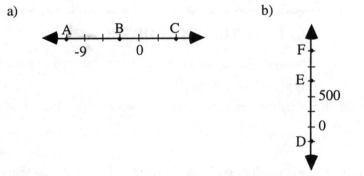

CHAPTER 1

AR-72.   Jane recorded the number of minutes she spent talking on the phone per day: 15, 25, 60, 10, 120, 85, 35, 20, 60, and 30. Make a stem-and-leaf plot to organize her data.

a)   Find the mean, median, and mode.

b)   If Jane wanted to convince her parents that she did not spend too much time on the phone, which of the measures of central tendency should she use?

c)   If her parents argued that they disagreed with her, what evidence could they use?

AR-73.   Follow your teacher's directions to do the Draw a Question activity. You will take turns drawing a slip of paper with a question on it from an envelope. Each person in your study team will give his or her answer to the question. Questions will be about the mathematics you have studied in this chapter and how you have studied it.

AR-74.   Bill and Kim played Rock-Paper-Scissors again to decide who has to wash the dishes. Bill suggested that they should stop using tile spacers and should just write down their scores using numbers. After a game they wrote:

Round	Bill	Kim
1	-3	2
2	1	-2
3	2	-3
4	-2	1
5	3	-1

a)   Write each player's game score as a sentence showing the sum of the five rounds.

b)   Who has to wash the dishes?

AR-75.

┌──┐
│   **INTEGERS**   │
│   │
│ **INTEGERS** are whole numbers and their opposites, including zero. These │
│ numbers can be positive, negative, or zero. On the number line, think of them as │
│ "whole steps."   │
│   │
│ ◄━●━━●━━●━━●━━●━━●━━●━━●━━●━━●━━●━━●━━●━━●━━●━━●━━●━━●━━●━►   │
│   -9 -8 -7 -6 -5 -4 -3 -2 -1 0 1 2 3 4 5 6 7 8 9 │
└──┘

Make these notes in your Tool Kit to the right of the double-lined box.

a)   Give an example of a number that is not an integer.

b)   List two real-world examples when you would use negative integers.

AR-76.   Use the number line shown below to find each of the following positions on the line.

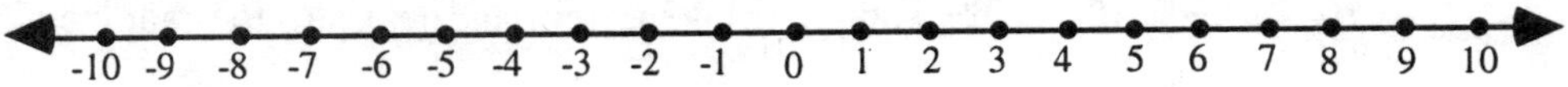

a)   4 more than -2   b)   3 more than -7

c)   2 less than 1   d)   8 more than -10

e)   5 less than -2

f)   On the number line above, is the number with the greater value farther to the right or to the left on the number line? Explain in a complete sentence.

AR-77.   Match each expression in the problem below to the correct part of the previous problem.

a)   3 + (-7)   b)   8 + (-10)   c)   4 + (-2)

d)   -2 – 5   e)   1 – 2

AR-78.   Use the number line to help answer the following questions.

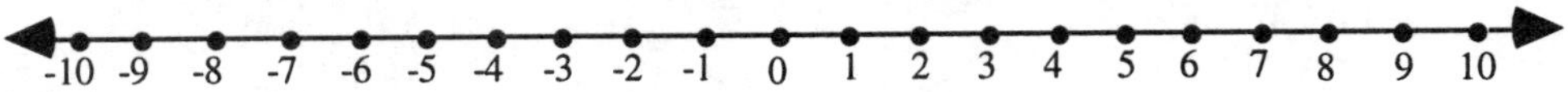

a)   What is the mean of 1 and 7?

b)   What number is halfway between 1 and 7 on the number line?

c)   What number is halfway between -5 and 1 on the number line?

d)   Is the answer in part (c) the mean of -5 and 1?

e)   What is half of -8?

AR-79.   What is the value of each expression? (Use a number line or tile spacers as needed.)
          Record your answer as an equation.

a)   -3 + (-4)   b)   -4 + 5   c)   3 + (-7)

AR-80.   Make a stem-and-leaf plot of the following test data: 64, 87, 52, 12, 17, 23, 45, 88,
          45, 92, 62, 76, 77, 34, 53, and 45.

a)   Find the mode.   b)   Find the median.

AR-81.   Complete the scales for the following axes on the resource page.

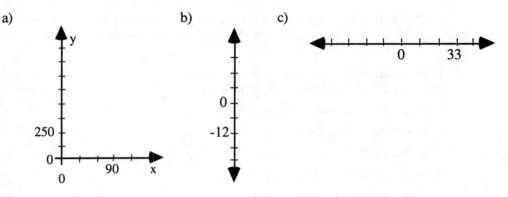

a)

b)

c)

AR-82.   What number is represented by each of the letters on the number lines below?

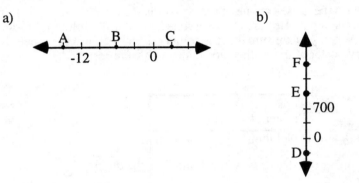

a)

b)

AR-83.   **Algebra Puzzles** Decide which number belongs in place of the variable to make the
equation true. Remember that $\frac{n}{3}$, for example, means the number n divided by 3. For
part (a), think, "What number divided by 3 gives the answer 4?"

a) $\frac{n}{3} = 4$ b) $\frac{n}{5} = 10$ c) $4n - 3 = 9$

AR-84.   Follow your teacher's directions for practicing mental math. Describe the strategy you
think is most difficult.

AR-85.   **Chapter Summary**

When you finish a chapter in a math course, you need to reflect on how well you have learned the material. It is time to think about all that you have studied and learned in this chapter.

Your teacher will be assigning topics to teams from the following list of problems from the chapter.

- Mean: AR-24, 25(c), 28(a), 60

- Mode: AR-28(b), 39(b)

- Median: AR-38(b), 39(c), 59

- Stem-and-leaf: AR-38(a), 39, 72

- Scaling graphs: AR-64, 65, 68

- Integers: AR-9, 74

- Complete graph: AR-46

With your partner or team, select one of the problems from the list that you think is a good example of the topic. Be sure that everyone has a correct solution for the problem in their notebook. When you are sure that the solution is correct, use the model below to create a summary poster of the mathematical idea you were assigned.

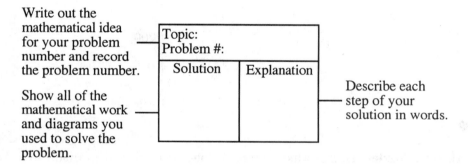

Write out the mathematical idea for your problem number and record the problem number.

Topic:
Problem #:

| Solution | Explanation |

Describe each step of your solution in words.

Show all of the mathematical work and diagrams you used to solve the problem.

AR-86.   Shelley surveyed her classmates to find out how much money they had in their pockets, wallets, and backpacks. The dollar amounts were $1, $2, $1, $1, $8, $1, $7, $10, and $5.

a)   What is the mode of these dollar amounts?

b)   If the person with the most money had $100 instead of $10, would the mode change? Why or why not?

c)   Would changing the largest amount of money change the median?

d)   What is the mean for the original dollar amounts?

e)   Would changing the largest amount to $100 change the mean? If your answer is yes, find the new mean. If not, explain why not.

AR-87.   Look at the bar graph below. It shows information about a soda machine.

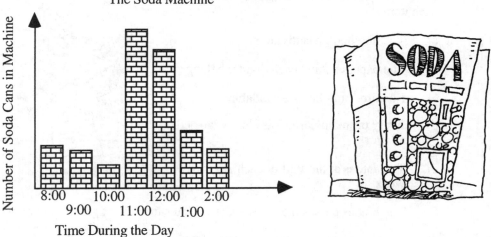

The Soda Machine

Number of Soda Cans in Machine (vertical axis)

8:00   10:00   12:00   2:00
  9:00   11:00   1:00

Time During the Day

a)   What is missing from the graph? Explain using a complete sentence.

b)   Explain in one or two complete sentences what happens to the soda cans in the vending machine throughout the school day.

c)   In a couple of sentences, give an explanation for what may have happened on this day according to the bar graph above.

AR-88.   Play another game of Rock-Paper-Scissors with a partner (a friend, a brother or sister, a parent, or a neighbor) and record your scores.

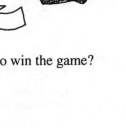

a)   How many rounds did you win?

b)   How many rounds did your partner win?

c)   What was your final score?

d)   What was your partner's final score?

e)   Who won the game (five rounds)?

f)   Did the person who won the greatest number of rounds also win the game?

AR-89. **Notebook Check**

Have your parent look at your notebook and score each item.

a) The notebook has dividers.

b) The papers behind each divider belong there.

c) Required supplies are available.

d) Every problem number is clearly labeled on all work.

e) The date is at the start of each day's new work.

f) The binder passes the "shake test." You can shake it **gently** and no papers fall out.

g) Student's name is on the inside of the binder cover.

h) Student's backpack does not have loose math papers in it.

i) The Tool Kit booklet is up to date.

AR-90. **What We Have Done in This Chapter**

Below is a list of the Tool Kit entries from this chapter.

- AR-5   Study Team Guidelines (also AR-12, 49, 66)
- AR-26   Mean
- AR-27   Mode
- AR-37   Median
- AR-44   Stem-and-Leaf Plot
- AR-45   A Complete Graph of Data
- AR-54   Measures of Central Tendency
- AR-69   Scaling the Axes of Graphs
- AR-75   Integers

Review all the entries and read the notes you made in your Tool Kit. Make a list of any questions, terms, or notes you do not understand. Ask your partner or study team members for help. If anything is still unclear, ask your teacher.

THE GAME SHOW

Chapter 2

Chapter 2
The Game Show: **INTEGERS and SOLVING EQUATIONS**

In Chapter 1, you played the game Rock-Paper-Scissors. In this chapter you will play more games to learn about integers and coordinate graphing. Your class will be holding a game show tournament at the end of the chapter. There is important mathematics to be learned through these games. Try to play your best. Learn the math strategies and secrets to playing well. By the end of the chapter, you will be able to:

- add positive and negative numbers.

- multiply positive and negative numbers.

- graph in the coordinate plane.

- find absolute value.

- solve equations.

Read the problem below, but **do not try to solve it now**. What you learn over the next few days will enable you to solve it.

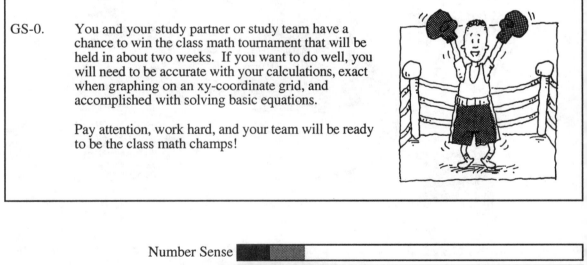

GS-0.   You and your study partner or study team have a chance to win the class math tournament that will be held in about two weeks. If you want to do well, you will need to be accurate with your calculations, exact when graphing on an xy-coordinate grid, and accomplished with solving basic equations.

Pay attention, work hard, and your team will be ready to be the class math champs!

Number Sense	
Algebra and Functions	
Mathematical Reasoning	
Measurement and Geometry	
Statistics, Data Analysis, & Probability	

Chapter 2
The Game Show: INTEGERS and GRAPHING

GS-1.   Follow your teacher's directions for practicing mental math.

GS-2.   With your partner, play one game of Rock-Paper-Scissors. Keep a written record, then answer the following questions.

   a)   Write the equation to find your final score.

   b)   Write the equation to find your partner's final score.

GS-3.   Use at least one tile to represent each integer below. Show your drawing.

   a)   5   b)   -4   c)   -7   d)   0

GS-4.   What number is represented by each tile drawing?

   a)   + − + −   b)   − − −   c)   + + − −
         + − +   + + +   − − − −
         + +   − − −
                               − − −

GS-5.   Represent each expression using tiles. Sketch each model and write the expression below it. Then simplify and write an equation for the answer. Be sure to draw in all the steps. Remember to circle the zero pairs.

Example: -7 + (-2) = -9

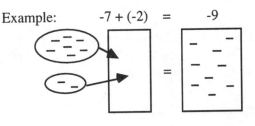

   a)   2 + (-4)   b)   -7 + (-7)

   c)   -3 + 5 + 3   d)   Did you see a quick way to do part (c)?

GS-6.   The problem -3 + 5 can be modeled two
ways. As a tile spacer problem it looks
like this:

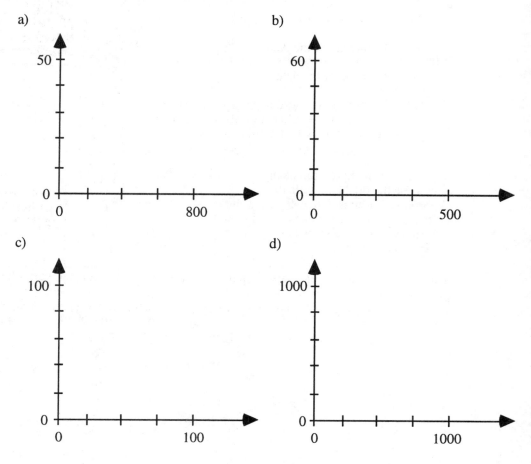

On a number line, this same problem
would mean "start at -3 and move up 5
spaces."

Do the following problems on the resource
page provided by your teacher.

a)   -8 + 2   b)   3 + (-4)   c)   -5 + 5   d)   -5 + (-3)

e)   7 + (-5)   f)   -4 + (-4)   g)   -4 + 5 + 4   h)   -4 + 8 + (-2)

GS-7.   Brittonie says that -2 + (-5) equals 7 because she heard that two negatives make a
positive, but Dante disagrees. Explain your position on this discussion.

Note: When the icon below the problem number at left appears, it indicates that there may
be one or more errors in the problem that the authors put there as part of the question.

GS-8.   Copy the axes and complete the scales.

a)

50

0
0   800

b)

60

0
0   500

c)

100

0
0   100

d)

1000

0
0   1000

GS-9. Tom says to you, "I am thinking of a number. Take that number and double it. When you add negative 6 to it, the result is zero. What's my number?"

Note: When you see the icon below the problem number at left, it indicates that you MAY NOT use a calculator for that problem.

GS-10. Add without a calculator.

a)
```
  4.37
+ 0.64
```

b)
```
  4.7
+ 0.67
```

c)
```
  4.34
+ 4.6
```

d)
```
  3.92
+ 0.0795
```

GS-11. Mrs. Libro-Amante is the school librarian. She has kept track of the number of books that have been checked out of the school library for each school day in the past month. The information is shown in the stem-and-leaf plot below right.

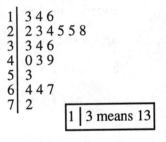

a) Find the mean of the data.

b) Find the median of the data.

c) Find the mode of the data.

d) Which measure of central tendency (the mean, median, or mode) would Mrs. Libro-Amante use if she wants to show that a large number of books are being checked out? Explain your reasoning.

```
1 | 3 4 6
2 | 2 3 4 5 5 8
3 | 3 4 6
4 | 0 3 9
5 | 3
6 | 4 4 7
7 | 2
```
| 1 | 3 means 13 |

GS-12. Now that we have started a new chapter, it is time for you to organize your binder.

a) Put the work from the last chapter in order and keep it in a separate folder.

b) When this is completed, write, "I have organized my binder."

GS-13.　Organized binders do not have loose papers in
them. The "shake test" is a technique you can
use to check that your papers are locked into
your binder. Hold your binder along the spine
and <u>gently</u> shake it. If any papers fall out, they
need to be hole-punched and inserted into the
rings of the binder. Work on your binder until
it passes the shake test. Look in the bottom of
your backpack. If there are any loose papers
there, they are in the wrong place. Take them
out and put them back into your binder. Write
"I have finished the shake test" next to this
problem number when you have finished it.

GS-14.　The different models we have used to add integers are summarized in the box below
using the example -5 + 2.

The problem -5 + 2 can be modeled two
ways. As a tile spacer problem it looks
like this:

On a number line, this same problem
would mean "start at -5 and move up 2
spaces."

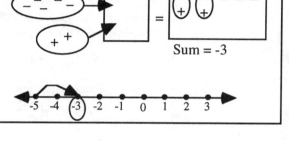

Sum = -3

Evaluate the following expressions.

a)　　-3 + 7

b)　　-7 + (-2)

c)　　16 + (-8)

d)　　-17 + (-9)

e)　　10 + (-60)

f)　　10 + (-6) + (-7) + 3 + (-2)

GS-15.   Use the resource page to play a game of Win-A-Row. Play one round of Rock-Paper-Scissors to determine who plays first.

Win-A-Row
A game for two players.

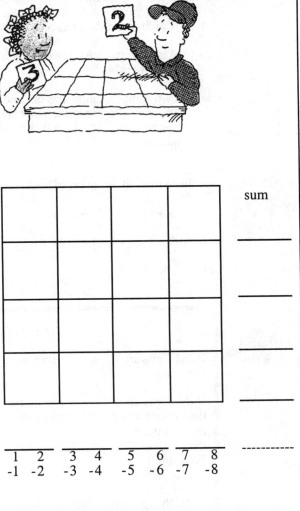

Mathematical Purpose: To add positive and negative integers.

Object: To place your numbers strategically on the game board so that you can win the largest number of rows.

Materials: One Win-A-Row game board.

Scoring: Once all the boxes in the table have been filled in, calculate the sum of each row and column. Every positive sum means one point for Player 1. Every negative sum means a point for Player 2.

How to Play the Game:
• Player 1 places one of the numbers 1, 2, 3, 4, 5, 6, 7, or 8 in the square of his/her choice then crosses that number from the list.
• Player 2 places one of the numbers -1, -2, -3, -4, -5, -6, -7, or -8 in another square then crosses that number from the list.
• Alternate the play until all the squares are full and all your numbers are used up.
• Add the numbers in each row and write the sum on the appropriate blank. Give the winner of each row one point.
• Add the numbers in each column and write the sum on the appropriate blank. Give the winner of each column one point.
• If the two players tie after adding the rows and columns, find the sum of the downward (from left to right) diagonal to decide the final winner.
• If the two players are still tied, find the sum of the other diagonal (up from left to right) to decide the final winner.
• If the game is still tied, you are both winners!

Ending the Game: The game ends when all the squares are full and you have found all of the sums.

GS-16.   After you have played a game of Win-A-Row, add all four of the horizontal totals. Next add all four of the vertical results. What do you notice? Explain your answer.

GS-17.   Two stem-and-leaf plots at right show the heights in centimeters of boys and girls who entered the classroom.

Height (centimeters)

Boys			Girls		
13	5		13	2	
14	9		14	3 6	
15	2 8 9		15	5 7	
16	7		16	1 2 4	
17			17		
18			18	5	
19	4				
20	1				

13 | 4 means 134 cm

a)   Which set of data has a larger range?

b)   What are the medians of the girls' and boys' heights?

c)   Two girls (heights: 168 cm and 187 cm) and a boy (height: 167 cm) came to class late. Recalculate the two medians.

GS-18.   Evaluate the following problems mentally.

a)   -3 + (-3) + (-3) + (-3)

b)   -12 + (-12) + (-12)

c)   -6 + (-6) + (-6) + (-6) + (-6)

d)   -5 + 5 + (-5)

e)   -15 + (-10)

f)   -11 + 20

ADDITION OF INTEGERS

If the signs are the same, combine by adding the value of each number and keep the same sign.

If the signs are different, ignore the signs. Then subtract the smaller number from the larger number and keep the sign of the original number that was farthest from zero on the number line.

Example 1:
    add -5 + (-3)
    5 + 3 = 8
    Both signs are –, so -5 + (-3) = -8

Example 2:
    add -4 + 2
    4 – 2 = 2
    -4 is farthest from 0,
    so -4 + 2 = -2

Put two examples of adding integers to the right of the double-lined box in your Tool Kit. One example must have at least one negative integer. When you return to class, have your partner or a teammate check that your examples are correct.

GS-19.   Do this problem in your head. Check your answer.

Maralena has a playing card in her hand. If she triples the number on the card and adds -1, the result is 11. What is the number on her card?

Explain how you found the number.

GS-20. Juan got on an elevator at the middle floor of a building, went up 4 floors, down 3 floors, up 1 floor, and down 9 floors, where he left the elevator on the first floor.

   a)   How many floors are in the building? You may want to draw a vertical number line to help you model this problem.

   b)   Explain how you found the number of floors.

GS-21. Jojo and Dano are working on Algebra Puzzles together.

   Jojo: Look out! There are more fractions in the Algebra Puzzles!

   Dano: Just think of a pizza for $\frac{P}{4} = 5$. P stands for the price of the whole pizza. Cut it into four equal parts, and each part costs $5.

   a)   How much does the whole pizza cost?

   b)   Use Dano's "pizza method." Draw a diagram to solve $\frac{K}{6} = 4$.

   c)   What mathematical operation did you use to get your answer for part (b)?

GS-22. **Algebra Puzzles** Solve the following Algebra Puzzles.

   a) $\frac{w}{3} = 7$ b) $\frac{m}{6} = 10$ c) $\frac{n}{5} = 10$

   d)   Explain what you did to get your answer to part (c).

GS-23. MNEEZ the Martian has typical Martian children who each have two heads and five legs. At a birthday party with Martian and Earth children, she counted 19 heads and 46 legs. How many Earth children and how many Martian children were at the party?

GS-24.   **Coordinate Walk Part A**

You and your classmates will walk to certain points on a coordinate grid forming three different graph patterns. Be sure to draw a dot where each student stands and label the point with an ordered pair (x, y). The first number in your ordered pair is the distance you walk along the horizontal x-axis. The second number is the distance you walk parallel to the vertical y-axis. You will plot all three patterns on the resource page your teacher gives you.

Example

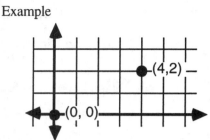

GS-25.   **Coordinate Walk Part B**

a)   During the first Coordinate Walk, what shape was created by the pattern of points?

b)   Were all the students standing the same distance from the origin, which is the point (0, 0)?

c)   During the second Coordinate Walk, what pattern or shape was created?

d)   At what point did this line cross the x-axis? Where did it cross the y-axis?

e)   Why was it easy to see if a student walked to an incorrect point?

f)   During the third Coordinate Walk, what did all the points have in common?

g)   Would you describe this third pattern as a horizontal or vertical line in relation to the axes?

GS-26.   You have walked to ordered pairs, graphed the points on paper, and written the points as (x, y) coordinates. On a sheet of graph paper, follow the directions below.

a)   Create and label the x- and y-axes.

b)   Label the origin.

c)   Graph the pattern $y = 3$. That is, plot many points that all have a y-value of 3.

d)   Would you describe this as a horizontal or vertical line?

e)   On this same grid, graph the pattern $y = x$. That is, plot and label any six points so that the x-value and y-value are the same. Points (-2, -2), (4, 4), and (0, 0) are examples of points on the line $y = x$.

f)   Describe this graph.

GS-27.

GRAPHING POINTS ON AN XY-COORDINATE GRID

Numerical data that you want to put on a two-dimensional graph is entered on the graph as **POINTS**.

The points on the graph are identified by two numbers, which together make an **ORDERED PAIR** written generally as (x, y). One example of an ordered pair is (3, 2). These two numbers are called **COORDINATES** because together they name the location of the point on the graph.

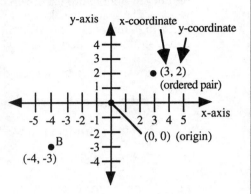

The first number of the ordered pair is the **X-COORDINATE** because it represents the horizontal distance from (0, 0).

The second number of the ordered pair is the **Y-COORDINATE** because it represents the vertical distance from (0, 0).

The ordered pair (3, 2) is located at a point that is right 3 units and up 2 units from the **ORIGIN**, (0, 0). The scaled lines are called the **X-AXIS** (horizontal) and **Y-AXIS** (vertical).

Make these notes in your Tool Kit to the right of the double lined box.

a)   Name the ordered pair for point B.

b)   Explain how to plot the ordered pair (-2, 1).

c)   Mark and label the point (-2, 1) in your Tool Kit.

GS-28.   Maria gets confused when she is asked to graph points. She does not know how the point (5, 0) differs from the point (0, 5). Write a short note to Maria that explains how to graph each of those points correctly.

GS-29.   Mrs. Fernandez is the owner of the local deli/drive-in. She has been keeping track of the number of double dip ice cream cones sold each week. (The second week ended with the day that had a high temperature of 102° F.) Two stem-and-leaf plots are shown at right.

1st week		2nd week	
1	9	1	9
2	5 6 7	2	5 6 7
3	6 9	3	6 9
4	2	4	
5		5	
6		6	
7		7	9

2nd week
1 | 9
means 19 cones

a)   How are the two data sets different?

b)   Find the range for each week.

c)   Find the mean for each week.

d)   Find the median for each week.

e)   Compare the two medians.

f)   Compare the two means.

g)   An **outlier** is a number in a data set that is either much higher or much lower than the other numbers in the set. Which measure of central tendency was affected by an outlier? Why?

h)   Why did the outlier not affect the median?

GS-30.   **Algebra Puzzles** Solve these Algebra Puzzles.

a) $6n = 24$

b) $\frac{n}{7} = 8$

c) $3x - 19 = 11$

d) $\frac{n}{3} = 6$

GS-31.   Using integer tiles, sketch a model and evaluate the following expressions.

a) $-5 + (-3)$

b) $6 + (-3)$

c) $-11 + 2$

d) $4 + (-10)$

e) $3 + (-9)$

f) $-2 + (-5)$

GS-32.   Evaluate the following expressions mentally.

a) $3 + 4 - 7$

b) $50 - 30 - 40$

c) $4 - 100$

d) $40 - 170$

GS-33.   In the Old West, a cowboy bought a horse for
         $100 in Laredo, sold it for $110 in El Paso,
         bought it back the next week for $120, and sold
         it again in Laredo for $130. How much money
         did he gain or lose?

GS-34.   Find each product.

a)   b)   c)   d)
    (4.2)(0.2)   (4.2)(0.04)   (13.6)(0.71)   (13.6)(3.73)

GS-35.   One way to organize coordinate point patterns is to make a $y = 2x$
         vertical table of x- and y-values.

a)   Complete this table where all the y-values are twice the
      x-values. The algebraic rule is $y = 2x$.

b)   Plot the ordered pairs on a coordinate grid.

x	y
-3	-6
-2	-4
-1	-2
0	
2	
3	

GS-36.   Mr. Dolan, the school principal, was looking at
         student surveys as he prepared a report for the
         school board. He noticed a clear relationship
         between the number of hours a student spends
         on the Internet or watching television each week
         and his/her grade point average (GPA). Here is
         the data that Mr. Dolan gathered.

Number of Hours on the Internet or Watching TV	38	6	21	17	30	2	14	40	9	9
Student's GPA	1.15	3.55	2.45	2.72	1.75	3.85	2.95	1.00	3.41	3.10

a)   Plot the points in the table above on the graph on the resource page. The result is
      called a **scatter plot**. The points are scattered over the graph because they came
      from data, not from a rule like "double the number" or $y = 2x$.

b)   What is the relationship between GPA and hours on the Internet or watching TV?

GS-37.   Play a game of Tug-O-War with a partner. Record the winner.

Tug-O-War
A game for two people.

Mathematical Purpose: To practice integer addition
                                      and multiplication.

Object: To be the first to reach the space marked
                 "Winner."

Materials: A resource page, a paper clip for the
                      spinner, two game markers, and a pencil.

Scoring: The first person to land exactly on the
                   "Winner" space wins the game.

How to Play the Game:

1. Start at zero.

2. Spin both spinners.
    • The "Groups of Steps" spinner
      determines how many times you may take
      your number of steps.
    • The "Number of Steps" spinner
      determines whether you move in a positive
      or negative direction and how many steps
      you will take.

3. Record your game on your paper in a chart
    like the one shown below.
    • Record your spins as a multiplication
      equation.
    • Record your new position as an addition
      equation.

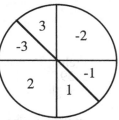

Groups of Steps

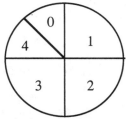

Number of Steps

Turn	Groups of Steps	Kind of Steps	Multiplication Problem	Your Position (addition problem)	Absolute Value (your distance from zero)
Example	3	-2	3(-2) = -6	0 + (-6) = -6	|-6| = 6

4. If your move would make your marker go off the board on any play, you lose your turn.

Ending the Game: The game ends when one player lands <u>exactly</u> on the "Winner" space.

GS-38.   Multiplication is:

(A) repeated addition   (B) repeated subtraction

(C) repeated division   (D) repeated multiplication

Note: The icon below the problem number above left indicates that the format of the problem is multiple choice.

GS-39.   In each of these problems, assume that the people divide the food evenly.

a)   If two people order one soda, how much of the soda should each person get?

b)   If two people order three hamburgers, how much should each person get?

c)   If three people order a large box of fries, what part is each person's share?

d)   Three people divide seven brownies. How many brownies should each person get?

e)   Two people order five apple turnovers. How many turnovers should each person get?

f)   If five people share three cartons of take-out food, what is each person's share?

GS-40.   **Algebra Puzzles** Each equation below represents one of the parts of problem GS-39. Decide which problem the equation represents and give the number that belongs in the place of the variable.

Sample solution to part (a): The equation $2x = 1$ represents 2 people, 1 soda, and each person's getting $\frac{1}{2}$ of the soda.

a) $2x = 1$ b) $3x = 1$ c) $2s = 5$

d) $2s = 3$ e) $3x = 7$ f) $5s = 3$

GS-41.   Evaluate either by drawing a picture or calculating mentally.

a) $-10 + (-8)$ b) $220 + (-14)$

c) $-2\frac{1}{2} + 2\frac{1}{2} + (-3)$ d) $75 + (-30) + 160 + (-29)$

GS-42. Inspect each data set. Without making a calculation, decide if each statement about the data set is true or false. Explain how you decided.

a)   True or False: "The set of 24, 25, 26, and 28 has a mean of 103."

b)   True or False: "The set of 0, 1, 2, 3, and 4 has no mode."

c)   True of False: "Fifteen is the median of this data set: 12, 14, 15, 13, and 16."

d)   True or False: "The mode of 0, 2, 2, 3, 4, and 5 is 5 because it has the greatest value."

GS-43.   Nadine and Diondra were working with fraction circles and were asked to represent thirds in two different ways. Their drawings are shown at right. Tanisha said, "One of the pictures is incorrect." Which picture is incorrect, and why is it incorrect?

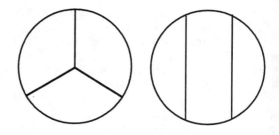

GS-44. Simplify without using a calculator.

a)   4.73 + 6.95 + 13.6 + 14   b)   25.6(10)

c)   3.65(100)   d)   (3.6)(3)(2.3)

GS-45. Follow your teacher's directions for practicing mental math.

GS-46. In the Tug-O-War game, was the answer greater or less than 0 when you multiplied a positive number of groups by a negative number of steps?

GS-47. Use the skills you learned in Tug-O-War to simplify.

a)   -5 + (-5) + (-5) + (-5) + (-5) + (-5) + (-5)

b)   7(-5)

c)   Adlai said, "Multiplication is like repeated addition." What does he mean?

GS-48.   Use the method shown in the box below to do the multiplication in parts (a) through (d).

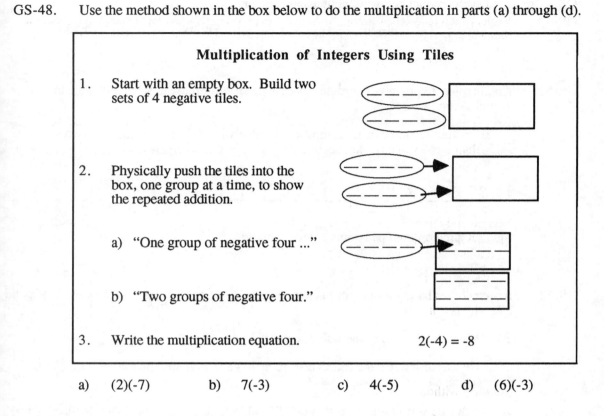

Multiplication of Integers Using Tiles

1.   Start with an empty box. Build two sets of 4 negative tiles.

2.   Physically push the tiles into the box, one group at a time, to show the repeated addition.

a) "One group of negative four ..."

b) "Two groups of negative four."

3.   Write the multiplication equation.   2(-4) = -8

a)   (2)(-7)   b)   7(-3)   c)   4(-5)   d)   (6)(-3)

GS-49.   Write the multiplication equation that corresponds with each drawing below.

a)   b)   c)

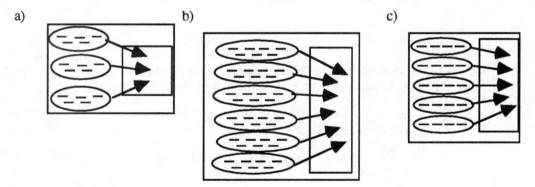

GS-50.   Draw a tile diagram for each product (as shown in problem GS-49) and write a multiplication equation.

a)   3(-4)   b)   5(-2)   c)   4(-1)   d)   6(0)

GS-51.   Find each product below without using a picture.

a)   (3)(-7)   b)   7(-12)   c)   13(-5)   d)   (9)(-8)

GS-52.   Another way to organize coordinate point patterns is to make a horizontal table of x- and y-values.

a)   On your resource page, complete this table where all the y-values are two more than the x-values. The algebraic rule is y = x + 2.

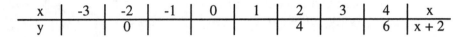

x	-3	-2	-1	0	1	2	3	4	x
y		0				4		6	x + 2

b)   Plot the ordered pairs on a coordinate grid.

GS-53.   Armando has an A average for his test scores. His test percentages so far are 96, 92, and 97.

a)   What is the mean of these three scores?

b)   He was absent for the fourth test, so he has a 0 on it until he makes it up. What is the mean of these four scores?

c)   Since he was doing so well before this missing test, he thinks that one missing test will not hurt his grade very much. Write him a short note explaining the effect this one zero has on his grade.

GS-54.   Calvin is tiling a floor. The dimensions of the floor are 8 feet by 6 feet. He wants to use 1-foot by 1-foot tiles.

a)   How many 1-foot by 1-foot tiles does Calvin need to buy to tile the floor?

b)   How many 6-inch by 6-inch tiles would it take to tile the floor?

GS-55.   Simplify.

a)   -8 + (-8) + (-8) + (-8)   b)   -8 · 4

c)   8(-3)   d)   -3 + (-3) + (-3) + (-3) +
                                            (-3) + (-3) + (-3)

e)   -14 + (-14) + (-14)   f)   3(-14)

g)   -7 + (-7) + (-7) + (-7)   h)   5(-7)

i)   4(-9)   j)   -9 + (-9) + (-9) + (-9)

GS-56.   **Algebra Puzzles** Decide which negative number belongs in place of the variable to make the equation true.

a) $6x = -42$ b) $7x +5 = -16$ c) $2m +3 = -7$

GS-57.   Calculate without using a calculator.

a)   b)   c)   d)
     13.62   14.0   13.6 $25 - 13.65$
   $-\ 3.69$ $-\ 7.7$ $-\ 7.52$

GS-58.   Gracie loves to talk on the phone, but her parents try to restrict her calls. They kept these records and showed them to Gracie. The minutes she spent on the phone each day were 120, 60, 0, 30, 15, 0, 0, 10, and 20.

a)   Find the mean, median, and mode for the information.

b)   Which measure of central tendency would give Gracie's parents the best evidence that Gracie spends too long on the phone?

c)   Which measure of central tendency would give Gracie evidence that she is not spending too long on the phone?

GS-59.   Verify that your answers to problem GS-55 are correct.

a)   Find the pairs of problems with the same answer.

b)   Write the pair down as an equation that shows that multiplication is repeated addition.

GS-60.   Solve these Algebra Puzzles. Be prepared to explain your method.

a) $8x - 7 = 41$ b) $\frac{x + 6}{2} + 5 = 15$

GS-61.   Follow the steps below.

    a)   Think of a number between 1 and 100.

    b)   Double it.

    c)   Add 5.

    d)   Write down your result.

    e)   Exchange this sum with your partner and determine your partner's original number. Write, "I think my partner's number is ___."

    f)   Show your solution to your partner to see if you are right. Write on your paper, "My partner's number was ___."

GS-62.   Angela said her answer for the previous problem was 33.5. Andre said that was impossible, but Corliss said she could use an equation to find the original number.

    a)   Use x to represent the number and steps (b) and (c) in the previous problem to write an expression equal to Angela's number.

    b)   "Now I can work backwards," said Corliss. The last instruction in the previous problem was, "Add 5." What should be Corliss's first step here?

    c)   Corliss used her work from part (b), and her result was a shorter equation. What did she write?

    d)   Then Corliss did the opposite of "doubling the number." What did she do?

    e)   What was her result in part (d)?

GS-63.   Follow the steps below.

    a)   Think of a number between 50 and 100.

    b)   Divide by 2.

    c)   Subtract 6.

    d)   Write down your result.

    e)   Exchange this sum with your partner and determine your partner's original number. Write, "I think my partner's number is ___."

    f)   Show your solution to your partner to see if you are right. Write, "My partner's number was ___."

GS-64. Several students started choosing strange numbers to challenge their partners. Lloyd said his answer was 43.95.

   a) Use x as a variable to write an equation that uses the steps in the preceding problem.

   b) What is the first step to work backwards?

   c) Write a shorter equation.

   d) What is the next step?

   e) What is the result?

GS-65.

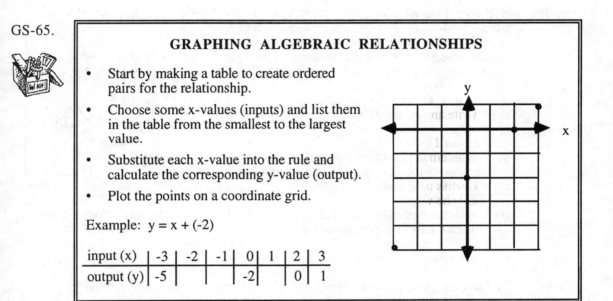

GRAPHING ALGEBRAIC RELATIONSHIPS

- Start by making a table to create ordered pairs for the relationship.
- Choose some x-values (inputs) and list them in the table from the smallest to the largest value.
- Substitute each x-value into the rule and calculate the corresponding y-value (output).
- Plot the points on a coordinate grid.

Example: $y = x + (-2)$

input (x)	-3	-2	-1	0	1	2	3
output (y)	-5			-2		0	1

Make these notes in your Tool Kit to the right of the double-lined box.

   a) Highlight the words "making a table," "choose some x-values," "substitute," "calculate," and "plot."

   b) Substitute the x-coordinates that have missing y-coordinates into the function and do the calculations to find the corresponding y-value.

   c) Plot these new points on the coordinate grid in your Tool Kit.

GS-66. Do this problem in your head, then check your answer.

   Dale is thinking of a number. If you cut the number in half, then add 2, the result is 8. What is Dale's number? How can you be sure your answer is correct?

GS-67. Algebraic relationships such as $y = 2x$ or $y = x + 2$ pair input values (x) with output values. When the equation is written as $y =$ _____ , the right side of the equation is called the **rule**.

a) On your resource page, complete this table for $y = \frac{x}{2}$.

input (x)	-4	-2	-1	0	2	4	5	6
output (y)	-2		-0.5		1			3

b) Plot the resulting ordered pairs.

GS-68. Helga got a job with Mt. Everest Tours as a Tour Guide, so she has to move to Katmandu, Nepal. The company will pay her a monthly housing allowance based on the average rent in Katmandu. The eight rentals she found cost 300, 420, 720, 420, 600, 500, 700, and 480 rupees per week.

a) What are the mean, median, and mode for these rents?

b) Which measure of central tendency would the company prefer to use for determining her housing allowance?

c) Which measure of central tendency would Helga report to the company if she wanted a more expensive rental to live in?

GS-69. Evaluate each sum or product by drawing a picture or by calculating mentally.

a) $(6)(-4)$

b) $-888 + 1263$

c) $-317 + 603 - 92$

d) $(5)(-3)$

e) $-2\frac{1}{2} + (-3\frac{1}{2}) + (-4)$

f) $2\frac{1}{2} \cdot (-8)$

g) $(5)(-7)$

h) $162 + (-205) + (-152)$

GS-70. **Algebra Puzzles** Decide which number belongs in place of the variable to make the equation true.

a) $\frac{a}{7} = 7$

b) $\frac{x}{6} = 6$

c) $9x + 1 = 82$

d) $8x + 3 = -61$

GS-71.   Represent each problem with at least two other numerical expressions. For example, $\frac{3}{4} + \frac{3}{4} + \frac{3}{4}$ could be $\frac{9}{4}$ or $2\frac{1}{4}$.

a) $\frac{1}{2} + \frac{1}{2} + \frac{1}{2} + \frac{1}{2} + \frac{1}{2}$ b) $3 \cdot \frac{1}{8}$

c) $5 \cdot \frac{1}{3}$ d) $\frac{1}{5} + \frac{1}{5} + \frac{1}{5} + \frac{1}{5}$

GS-72.   Simplify.

a)   13.5(6.2)   b)   14.02 − 7.653

c)   25 + 63 + 12.952   d)   6.3 ÷ 3

GS-73.   Guillermo chose a number, multiplied it by 5, added 2, and got 22. Work backward to find Guillermo's mystery number.

GS-74.   When Thu and Juan work backward to solve Algebra Puzzles, they call it the "cover-up method." Read the dialogue below with your partner to see how Thu and Juan solve the Algebra Puzzle $5x + 2 = 22$.

Thu: Cover up the $5x$ because it has the variable. Two added to what number makes 22? $5x + 2 = 22$

Juan: Two added to 20 makes 22. I got 20 by using the inverse of addition; I subtracted 2 from 22. So $5x = 20$. $5x = 20$

Thu: The term we covered still has the variable, so now cover up just the variable. What number multiplied by 5 equals 20?

Juan: I get 4 for x. I used the inverse of multiplication and divided 20 by 5. $x = 4$

Thu: Now we have to show that our work is correct. Put 4 in place of x and simplify. It does equal 22. $5(4) + 2 = 20 + 2$
$= 22$

Juan: Mrs. Oribello calls that "checking by substitution" because you replace x with its equivalent value, 4.

Take turns with your partner using the cover-up method to solve the equations below. Use substitution to check your answers. Show your check.

>>Problem continues on the next page.>>

Partner #1		Partner #2	
a)	$5x + 3 = 13$	b)	$4x - 5 = 23$
c)	$\frac{x}{3} - 8 = 12$	d)	$\frac{c}{2} + 7 = 10$
e)	$301m + 205 = 2011$	f)	$502x - 402 = 1104$
g)	$20x + 14 = 354$	h)	$20x - 14 = 286$

 GS-75.

SOLVING EQUATIONS USING INVERSE OPERATIONS

Addition and subtraction are inverse operations. Multiplication and division are inverse operations.

The order of operations in the equation $5x + 7 = 37$ is to multiply by 5 and then add 7 to get 37. To solve the equation, work backward using the **INVERSE OPERATIONS.** First subtract 7 to get 30, then divide by 5 to get 6.

Check the solution by substituting 6 into the original equation for x: $5(6) + 7 = 37$

Make these notes in your Tool Kit to the right of the double-lined box.

a) What are the arithmetic operations in the equation?

b) State the first inverse operation you would use to solve the equation.

c) State the next inverse operation you would use to solve the equation.

 GS-76.

ABSOLUTE VALUE

ABSOLUTE VALUE is the distance a number is from zero on the number line in either direction. We use the symbol |x| to indicate the absolute value of any number x. For example,

$$|-3| = 3 \text{ and } |3| = 3.$$

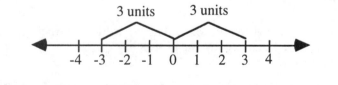

Make these notes in your Tool Kit to the right of the double-lined box.

If you take two steps forward (+2) or two steps backward (-2), you still take two steps. The absolute value of your movements is 2. Give two other real-world examples of absolute value.

GS-77.   Use the number line to help you determine the absolute value in the problems below.

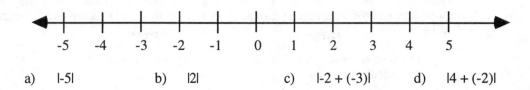

a) |-5| b) |2| c) |-2 + (-3)| d) |4 + (-2)|

GS-78.   Make a number line on your paper.

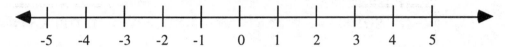

Plot the letters at the correct location(s) on your number line. For example, |B| = 2. Since |2| = 2 and |-2| = 2, you would plot a B above -2 and 2.

a) |R| = 4   b) |A| = 1   c) |D| = 0

GS-79.   You have done several problems with coordinate graphing. Explain how to plot the point (-3, -2).

GS-80.   **Algebra Puzzles** Solve each equation. Show your steps.

a)   3x - 8 = 31   b)   31 = 4y + 3

c)   19 + 8y = 83   d)   2x + 7 = 10

GS-81.   Evaluate each expression by either drawing a picture or by calculating mentally.

a)   -4 + 6 + (-3)   b)   6(-3)

c)   9 + (-2)   d)   74 + (-93) + 18

e)   5(-4) + 5   f)   4(-2) + (-3)

g)   3(-5) + 2   h)   -50 + (-45) + (-35)

GS-82. An algebraic rule is an expression that operates with input values (x) to produce output values (y). A table is a good way to organize the coordinate points which may then be plotted on an xy-coordinate grid to produce the graph of the relationship between x and y.

a) On your resource page, create a table to organize a set of points for the relationship $y = 3x + 1$.

x	-4	-3	-2	-1	0	1	2	3	4
y	-11								

b) Graph the ordered pairs on an xy-coordinate grid.

GS-83. Today Mrs. Libro-Amante is looking at her records for the number of math books destroyed each year. She knows that the average price for the replacement books is $15. You need to help her decide how much she should plan to spend next year. Over the past ten years, 43, 35, 67, 32, 46, 23, 62, 29, 65, and 43 books have been destroyed.

a) Make a stem-and-leaf plot for the data.

b) Find the mean.

c) Find the mode.

d) Find the median.

e) Which measure of central tendency best describes the data for the destroyed books? Explain.

f) How much money should she expect to spend to replace the destroyed books? Exp

GS-84. **Chapter Summary** When you finish a chapter, you need to summarize the material. This chapter had five objectives, which are listed at the front of the chapter.

a) Write the name of the first objective: "add positive and negative numbers."

b) Using your own words, explain what the objective means.

c) Select a representative problem of that objective from the chapter and copy the problem.

d) Using complete sentences, explain how to solve the problem.

e) Repeat this process for the other four objectives: "multiply positive and negative numbers," "coordinate graphing," "absolute value," and "solving equations."

GS-85.  Evaluate each expression either by drawing a picture of the operations or by calculating mentally.

a) -8 + 12 + (-4)

b) 5(-3)

c) 16 + (-15) + (-4)

d) 4(-6)

e) 8(-4) + (-15)

f) (-9)3

GS-86. Evaluate each sum or product either by drawing a picture or by calculating mentally.

a) 8 + (-6) + 4

b) -15 + 3 + 6

c) -8 + 12 + 2

d) 6(-8)

e) 5(-9)

f) -61 + (-13)

g) 4(-7)

h) 120 + (-15)

GS-87. Mrs. Libro-Amante, your school librarian, asks you to conduct a survey of how many books students read during the year. You get the following results: 12, 24, 10, 36, 12, 21, 35, 10, 8, 12, 15, 20, 18, 25, 21, and 9.

a) Use the data to create a stem-and-leaf plot.

b) Calculate the mean, median, and mode for the data.

c) Which measure of central tendency would you use to encourage students to read more books? Explain.

GS-88. Copy the axes below and complete the scales.

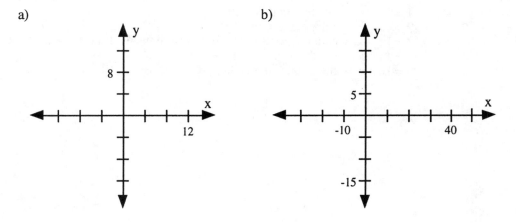

a)

b)

GS-89.   **Algebra Puzzles** Work backward or use the cover up method to solve these equations. Write the steps.

a) $\dfrac{x}{5} - 4 = -8$

b) $3x - 12 = -33$

c) $-30 = 3x - 6$

d) $7 + 5x = 42$

GS-90.   Complete your chapter summary if you did not complete it in class.

GS-91.   **Self-Evaluation** When you finish a chapter, you need to reflect on how well you have learned the material. One way to check your understanding at the end of a chapter is to try a problem from each objective and then evaluate your confidence with that objective. Try these five problems which match the five objectives from this chapter.

a)   Try this integer addition problem: $(-32) + (-18)$

b)   Try this integer multiplication problem: $6(-8)$

c)   Try this coordinate graphing problem: What is the coordinate of the point shown in the graph at right?

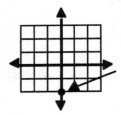

d)   Try this absolute value problem: What is the sum of $|-4|$ and $|4|$?

e)   Try solving this equation for m: $2m - 10 = -6$.

f)   Your teacher will tell your class the answers to the five questions. After you check your answers, write the objective name and then use the scale described below. For example, you might write, "Integer addition ability, understanding level 3." The objectives were "integer addition," "integer multiplication," "coordinate graphing," "absolute value," and "solving equations."

On a scale of 1 through 5, evaluate your understanding of each chapter objective.

1 = I do not understand this skill.
2 = I do not understand it well.
3 = I usually understand this idea, but I might need a little more practice.
4 = I understand this topic quite well.
5 = Bring on the quiz! I understand this idea very well.

GS-92.   **The Game Show**

Your teacher will assign you to a team and give you a
color-coded card labeled with a number. The color
represents your team. The number is your player
number. When your teacher calls your number, it
will be your turn to work with another student on
your team to answer the question correctly.

Your teacher will assign your team a space on the
board. Be sure you work in that space only. Follow
all rules concerning replacing the chalk or marker,
circling the answer and erasing your work after the
points for your work have been awarded. You will lose points if you forget. Appoint
a scorekeeper for your team.

When you are a member of the audience, remember that yelling or blurting out an answer
will cause your team to lose points.

The Game Show
A team game.

Mathematical Purpose: To review integer addition and multiplication, coordinate
graphing, solving equations, and absolute value.

Object: To solve math problems correctly and earn your team the most points.

Materials: Game show resource page to record a complete and correct solution.

Scoring:
   Earning points:
   • The first team to finish the problem correctly earns 400 points.
   • The second team to finish correctly earns 300 points.
   • The third team to finish correctly earns 200 points.
   • The fourth team to finish correctly earns 100 points.
   • Teams that do not complete the problem receive no points.
   • Teams that get their resource page 100% correct get a bonus of 1000 points.
   Losing points (penalties):
   • Answer blurted out by other team members—deduction of 100 points.
   • Leaving the board without erasing—deduction of 100 points.
   • Errors on team resource page—deduction of 100 points per error.

How to Play the Game:
   • Two players from each team will answer a question at the board. The
   remaining players will work the problem on the resource page.
   • For each question:
      1. Show the steps needed to arrive at a complete and correct solution.
      2. Write the units for your answers, if needed.
      3. Circle or box the answer.
      4. Place chalk in the tray (or cap marker).

Ending the Game: The game is over when your teacher calls time. All resource
                       pages from each team will be collected, and one will be
                       scored for each team. The team with the highest score wins the
                       game.

If there are no further questions, it is time to play. Good luck!

GS-93.   Carson got on an elevator on the first floor. She went up 6 floors, up 2 more floors, dow
          3 floors, and up 5 floors, where she left the elevator on the middle floor of the building.

          a)   Represent this problem as the sum of five integers.

          b)   How many floors are in the building?

          c)   Explain how you determined the number of floors.

GS-94.   Find the perimeter of each of the following figures. Remember that **perimeter** is the
          distance around a figure.

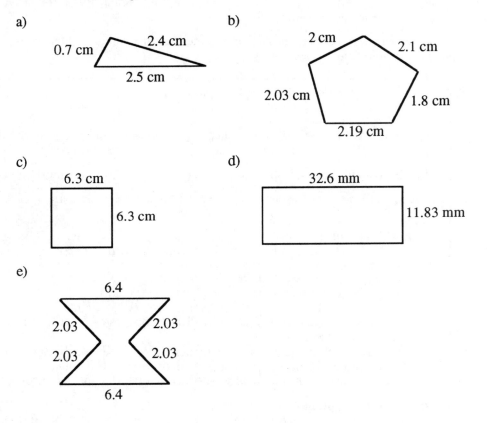

          a)

                                    2.4 cm
              0.7 cm

                        2.5 cm

          b)

                        2 cm
                                        2.1 cm

              2.03 cm
                                    1.8 cm

                        2.19 cm

          c)

              6.3 cm

                        6.3 cm

          d)

                    32.6 mm

                                11.83 mm

          e)

                    6.4

              2.03   2.03

              2.03   2.03

                    6.4

GS-95.   Create a table to organize a set of points that follow the rule $y = -3$. Graph the ordered
          pairs on a coordinate grid.

GS-96.   **Algebra Puzzles** Solve each equation. One answer includes a fraction.

          a) $13 = 3 + \frac{x}{7}$ b) $5x - 7 = -12$

          c) $3x - 6 = -27$ d) $2x - 4 = -15$

GS-97. The test grades for Mrs. Olson's math class are shown at right.

a) What is the class average (mean)?

b) What is the median?

c) What is (are) the mode(s)?

d) Is the mode useful for showing central tendency in this case? Explain.

1	0
4	0
5	
6	0 3 5
7	2 2 5 5 8 9
8	0 0 1 5 5
9	0 2 2 5 6 8

GS-98. Mrs. Libro-Amante is looking at the number of novels lost each year. She knows that the average price for the replacement books is $6.32. You need to help her decide how much she should plan on spending next year. Over the past ten years students have lost 34, 53, 76, 23, 64, 32, 26, 26, 56, and 93 novels, respectively.

a) Make a stem-and-leaf plot for the data.

b) Find the mean.

c) Find the mode.

d) Find the median.

e) If Mrs. Libro-Amante wants to estimate how many novels will be lost next year, which measure of central tendency should she use? Why?

f) How much money should she expect to spend next year? Why?

GS-99. **What We Have Done in This Chapter**

Below is a list of the Tool Kit entries from this chapter.

- GS-18   Addition Of Integers
- GS-27   Graphing Points on an xy-coordinate Grid
- GS-65   Graphing Algebraic Relationships
- GS-75   Solving Equations Using Inverse Operations
- GS-76   Absolute Value

Review all the entries and read the notes you made in your Tool Kit. Make a list of any questions, terms, or notes you do not understand. Ask your partner or study team members for help. If anything is still unclear, ask your teacher.

The Pig Race

Chapter 3

Chapter 3
The Pig Race: ORDER OF OPERATIONS AND MORE INTEGERS

One reason that mathematics is a universal language is that everyone agrees to do certain basic operations in the same order. In this chapter you will review and practice how to simplify mathematical expressions using standard procedures. This work will also give you an opportunity to practice your skills with arithmetic operations with integers. You will also learn how to create a table of organized information from a word problem so that you can use the table to solve the problem.

In this chapter you will have the opportunity to:

- use Guess and Check tables to solve word problems.

- evaluate expressions using the order of operations.

- learn to subtract integers.

- learn to multiply negative numbers.

- write numerical expressions and equations to represent situations.

- write equivalent forms of fractions, decimals and percents.

Read the problem below, but **do not try to solve it now**. What you learn over the next few days will enable you to solve it.

PR-0. **The Pig Race**

Throughout this chapter you will look at the relationships between numbers and learn how to write expressions to describe the relationships quickly and accurately. To do well in the Pig Race you will need to be able to solve problems like writing an arithmetic expression using the numbers 1, 2, 3, and 4 to get 51.

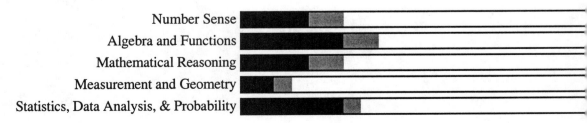

Number Sense

Algebra and Functions

Mathematical Reasoning

Measurement and Geometry

Statistics, Data Analysis, & Probability

Chapter 3
The Pig Race: ORDER OF OPERATIONS AND MORE INTEGERS

PR-1.   Welcome to the County Fair! Test your skills at the Dart Booth, shown below. Read the description of the game, then complete parts (a) and (b) below.

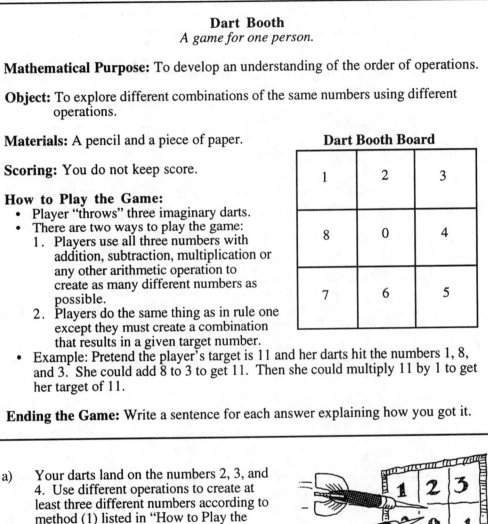

Dart Booth
A game for one person.

Mathematical Purpose: To develop an understanding of the order of operations.

Object: To explore different combinations of the same numbers using different operations.

Materials: A pencil and a piece of paper.

Scoring: You do not keep score.

How to Play the Game:
- Player "throws" three imaginary darts.
- There are two ways to play the game:
  1. Players use all three numbers with addition, subtraction, multiplication or any other arithmetic operation to create as many different numbers as possible.
  2. Players do the same thing as in rule one except they must create a combination that results in a given target number.
- Example: Pretend the player's target is 11 and her darts hit the numbers 1, 8, and 3. She could add 8 to 3 to get 11. Then she could multiply 11 by 1 to get her target of 11.

Dart Booth Board

1	2	3
8	0	4
7	6	5

Ending the Game: Write a sentence for each answer explaining how you got it.

a)   Your darts land on the numbers 2, 3, and 4. Use different operations to create at least three different numbers according to method (1) listed in "How to Play the Game" above.

b)   Write a sentence for each answer explaining how you got it.

PR-2.   Read the following problem and try to help Ramon and Kyle. They are weighing in their sheep at the county fair. Ramon notices that his sheep weighs 15 pounds more than Kyle' Together the two sheep weigh 205 pounds. How much does Kyle's sheep weigh?

Sometimes the easiest way to get started on a word problem is just to guess a possible answer and then check to see how close you are. Guessing is a good strategy if you use the results of each guess to systematically narrow down guesses to reach the correct answer. Use the problem below as a model of how to use a table to organize your guesses and how to use your guesses to find the correct answer.

Step 1:   Read the problem again. With some problems it is helpful to sketch a picture.

Step 2:   Set up a table. Decide what it is you want to know. In this case, you want to know how much Kyle's sheep weighs. This is what you will be guessing. Put this guess in the first column.

Guess Weight of Kyle's Sheep	

Guess the weight of Kyle's sheep. Try guessing 70 pounds. (70 is an easy number with which to work, and it makes sense, since the two sheep together weigh 205 pounds.) Put your guess in the box under the title, "Guess Weight of Kyle's Sheep."

Guess Weight of Kyle's Sheep	
70	

Step 3:   If you know that Kyle's sheep weighs 70 pounds, you can use this number to find how much Ramon's sheep weighs. Since the problem states that it weighs 15 pounds more than Kyle's sheep, calculate the weight of Ramon's sheep, then label the heading for the second column.

Guess Weight of Kyle's Sheep	Weight of Ramon's Sheep	
70	(70) + 15 = 85	

Step 4:   Now that you have the possible weights for both Kyle's and Ramon's sheep, you can calculate the total weight and label the third column "Total Weight of Both Sheep."

Guess Weight of Kyle's Sheep	Weight of Ramon's Sheep	Total Weight of Both Sheep	
70	(70) + 15 = 85	(70) + (85) = 155	

Step 5:   Label and use the last column to check whether the two sheep together weigh 205 pounds. If they do not weigh 205 pounds, write in the box whether the amount is too high or too low. If they do weigh 205 pounds, write "correct."

Guess Weight of Kyle's Sheep	Weight of Ramon's Sheep	Total Weight of Both Sheep	Check 205
70	(70) + 15 = 85	(70) + (85) = 155	too low

>>Problem continues on the next page.>>

Step 6: Start over with a new guess and use the same columns. Since the last guess was too low, Kyle's sheep must weigh more than 70 pounds. Try guessing 75 pounds and complete the second row of the table.

Guess Weight of Kyle's Sheep	Weight of Ramon's Sheep	Total Weight of Both Sheep	Check 205
70	(70) + 15 = 85	(70) + (85) = 155	too low
75	(75) + 15 = 90	(75) + (90) = 165	too low

Step 7: Seventy-five pounds turned out to be a little closer, but since it produced a total weight of 165 pounds, it is still far too low. For the next guess, choose a significantly greater weight: 100 pounds. Complete the third row.

Guess Weight of Kyle's Sheep	Weight of Ramon's Sheep	Total Weight of Both Sheep	Check 205
70	(70) + 15 = 85	(70) + (85) = 155	too low
75	(75) + 15 = 90	(75) + (90) = 165	too low
100	(100) + 15 = 115	(100) + (115) = 215	too high

Step 8: One hundred pounds is too high, but now we know that the answer is between 75 and 100 pounds and that 100 pounds is closer to the correct total weight. Try 95 pounds.

Guess Weight of Kyle's Sheep	Weight of Ramon's Sheep	Total Weight of Both Sheep	Check 205
70	(70) + 15 = 85	(70) + (85) = 155	too low
75	(75) + 15 = 90	(75) + (90) = 165	too low
100	(100) + 15 = 115	(100) + (115) = 215	too high
95	(95) + 15 = 110	(95) + (110) = 205	correct

Step 9: Congratulations! You have found the correct answer. Now you have only one thing left to do. Write a complete sentence that answers the question asked in the problem: Kyle's sheep weighs 95 pounds.

PR-3. I am thinking of a number. If you add 3 to the number and then multiply the sum by 4, you get 48. What is my number? Solve by copying and continuing the Guess and Check table below and continuing the process to solve the problem.

Guess the Number	Add 3 to the Number	Multiply Sum by 4	Check 48
5	(5) + 3 = 8	$4 \cdot (8) = 32$	too low

PR-4. Copy and complete the Guess and Check table below to solve the following problem. Remember to write the answer in a sentence.

I am thinking of a number. First multiply it by 5, then subtract 8. The result is 77. What is my number?

Guess Number	Multiply by 5	Subtract 8	Check 77
10	$(10) \cdot 5 = 50$	(50) − 8 = 42	too small

PR-5.

SOLVING PROBLEMS WITH GUESS AND CHECK TABLES

Step 1: Read the problem carefully. Make notes or sketch a picture to organize the information in the problem.

Step 2: Look at the question being asked. Decide what you are going to guess. Set up a table. Leave extra space for more columns in case you need them.

Step 3: Calculate the entry for a column and label the column.

Step 4: Continue the table until the check is correct.

Step 5: Write the answer in a complete sentence.

Example:

1. Kaitlin went to the fair. It costs $5 to get in. Tickets for the rides cost $1.25 each. How many rides did she go on if she spent a total of $26.25?

2. Guess Number of Rides	Money Spent on Rides	Total Money Spent at Fair	Check $26.25
3. 10	$(10) \cdot 1.25 = \$12.50$	$(\$12.50) + \$5 = \$17.50$	too low
4. 20	$(20) \cdot 1.25 = \$25.00$	$(\$25.00) + \$5 = \$30.00$	too high
15	$(15) \cdot 1.25 = \$18.75$	$(\$18.75) + \$5 = \$23.75$	too low
17	$(17) \cdot 1.25 = \$21.25$	$(\$21.25) + \$5 = \$26.25$	correct

5. Kaitlin went on 17 rides and her total cost at the fair was $26.25.

Answer the questions below in your Tool Kit to the right of the double-lined box.

a) What is the easiest part of using Guess and Check tables?

b) What is the hardest part of using Guess and Check tables?

PR-6.   Compute.

a)   6 + (-2)   b)   -7 + (-7)   c)   1 + (-4)

d)   -42 + 11 + (-3)   e)   15 · (-9)   f)   add 5 groups of (-16)

PR-7.   Find each of the following values.

a) |-12| b) |15|

c) |9| d) |-8|

PR-8.   **Algebra Puzzles** Solve these equations.

a) $5x - 23 = -23$ b) $13 + x = 0$

c) $2x + 14 = 0$ d) $-3 = x + 1$

PR-9.   At right is a stem-and-leaf plot for the weight of each book in Jenna's backpack, measured in ounces. After third period, Jenna realized that her heavy science book (64 oz) and her paperback romance novel (11 oz) were not in her bag. She called home to have her mom bring them to her at lunch. The weight of her backpack will change.

```
1 | 2 8
2 | 0 6 9
3 | 5 5
4 |
5 |
6 |
```

1	2 8

Means there are 2 books which weigh 12 and 18 oz

Think about how the addition of the two books will affect measures of central tendency. Will each increase, decrease, or stay the same? Select the word which best describes the change and write a complete sentence on your paper. You should be able to do this problem without calculating.

a)   The mean will _____.   b)   The median will _____.

c)   The mode will _____.   d)   The range will _____.

PR-10.   Use a ruler to draw a rectangle with a width of 3 centimeters and a length twice as long as the width. Find the perimeter of the rectangle. You may use the corner of a piece of paper or an index card to make square corners.

PR-11.   Maria was putting together party favors for her niece's birthday party. In each bag she put three small chocolate candies and four hard candies.

a)   How many candies did she put in each bag?

b)   If Maria had ten bags, how many candies did she use in all?

c)   In order to represent the total number of candies in ten bags, we write the expression $10 \cdot (3 + 4)$. What expression would we write to represent the total number of candies used if Maria had to make up 12 bags of favors?

PR-12. Now that we have started a new chapter, it is time for you to organize your binder.

a) Put the work from the last chapter in order and keep it in a separate folder.

b) When this is completed, write, "I have organized my binder."

PR-13. Use the numbers given in the table below and any arithmetic operation or combination of operations (addition, subtraction, multiplication, division) to find the given target number. When you have found a solution, explain in words how you combined the numbers. See the example in the table below. Copy and complete the table.

Numbers	Target Number	Solution Using Words
2, 3, 5	17	Multiply 5 times 3, then add 2.
1, 2, 4	9	
2, 3, 5	25	
2, 3, 9	12	

PR-14. You used integer tiles in Chapter 2. Build a tile model of the following situations and draw a sketch of your model.

a) Show -6 using at least ten tiles.

b) Show zero using four or more tiles.

c) Is it possible to represent zero using exactly five tiles? Why or why not?

PR-15. A **zero pair** has one postive tile and one negative tile. A **neutral field** is made of one or more zero pairs. Build and draw the following.

a) Start with a neutral field of six zero pairs. Remove four positive tiles. What is left?

b) Start with a neutral field of ten zero pairs. Remove eight negative tiles. What is left?

c) Write a subtraction problem for part (a).

d) Write a subtraction problem for part (b).

PR-16. Using the following examples as models, draw and solve the problems in parts (a) through (i) below.

For -4 – (-6):

1. Start with -4 and a neutral field.

2. Remove (-6).

3. Write the equation.

Record this:

$-4 – (-6) = 2$

For 3 – (-5):

1. Start with 3 and a neutral field.

2. Remove (-5).

3. Write the equation.

$3 – (-5) = 8$

a) $0 – 8$

b) $0 – (-8)$

c) $0 – (-2)$

d) $-12 – (-5)$

e) $0 – 10$

f) $-6 – (-1)$

g) $-8 – 2$

h) $-1 – (-9)$

i) $5 – (-5)$

j)   Why do we need to start with a neutral field on certain subtraction problems?

PR-17. Greg, Rick, and Cory met at a Civil War reenactment exercise. The characters they played were three brothers, each a year older than the next. When their ages were added, the sum was 84. Greg was the oldest, and Cory was the youngest. How old are the three characters?

Guess Cory's Age	Cory's Age + 1 year = Rick's Age	Cory's Age + 2 years = Greg's Age	Sum of all 3 ages	Check Sum = 84
10	(10) + 1 = 11	(10) + 2 = 12	(10) + (11) + (12) = 33	too low

PR-18. Draw a rectangle as described below.

a)   Use a ruler to draw a rectangle with a $2\frac{1}{2}$ -inch length and a $1\frac{1}{2}$ -inch width.

b)   Find the perimeter of the rectangle. Remember that perimeter is the distance around a shape.

PR-19.   Ahmed went to the fair. He brought $23 and spent all of his time at the Dart Booth. If it cost $5 to get in and $1.50 each time he played the Dart Booth, how many games could he play?

Guess Number of Games Played	Money Spent on Darts	Total Money Spent at the Fair	Check $23
5	(5) · $1.50 = $7.50	($7.50) + $5 = $12.50	too low

PR-20.   Simplify the following expressions. Draw the integer tiles. Sometimes you will need to start with a neutral field.

a)   -2 – 0   b)   0 – (-4)   c)   0 – 2

d)   -8 – (-6)   e)   -8 – 6   f)   8 – (-6)

g)   -15 – 4   h)   -15 – (-4)   i)   15 – (-4)

PR-21.   Make integer tile drawings for the following questions.

a)   Start with -4, then subtract -3. What is left? Do you need a neutral field? Why or why not?

b)   Start with -4 and a neutral field of at least three zeros. Now subtract -6. What is left? Write a subtraction equation to show what you did.

c)   How do you know when you need a neutral field to subtract an integer? Include an example that is different from the ones in this problem.

PR-22.   Thomas Jefferson wrote the Declaration of Independence in a year in which the tens and hundreds digits are equal and in which the ones and thousands digits have a sum equal to one of the middle digits. The entire digit sum is 21. In what year was the Declaration written?

PR-23.   **Algebra Puzzles**   Decide which negative number belongs in place of the variable to make each equation true.

a) $5x + 1 = -9$

b) $2x + 5 = -3$

PR-24.   Follow your teacher's directions for practicing mental math. Write the strategy that seems most efficient.

PR-25.   **Equivalent expressions** may appear different, but they actually have the same value.

$$0.50 = \frac{50}{100} \qquad \frac{50}{100} = \frac{1}{2} \qquad \frac{50}{100} = 50\%$$

You will need a fraction-decimal-percent transparency grid. Think of your grid as 1 or one whole or 100%.

a)   How many small squares are on your grid?

b)   What fraction of the area of your grid is one small square?

c)   Write the area of one small square in decimal form. (It may help to think of money.)

d)   Remember that "percent" is a word that means "out of one hundred." When you earn 100% on a 100-point test you have earned 100 points out of 100 possible. Write the area of one small square as a percent.

e)   Your answers to parts (b), (c), and (d) are equivalent ways to describe the area of one square on the fraction-decimal-percent grid. Write them as equivalent values like this: fraction = decimal = percent.

PR-26.   Place your fraction-decimal-percent grid on top of box (i) below. You can write several equivalent expressions to describe the shaded area in box (i) such as $\frac{25}{100} = \frac{1}{4}$, 0.25 (like money), and 25%.

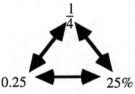

a)   Place your fraction-decimal-percent grid on top of box (ii), then box (iii) below. Think of your grid as representing the number 1 or one whole.

b)   How much of the grid is shaded in each box? Make an arrow triangle like the one above, naming a fraction, a decimal, and a percent for <u>each</u> box. Compare your results with your partner or teammates.

i)   ii)   iii)

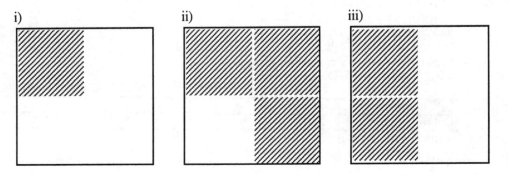

PR-27.   Use the resource page your teacher gives you or make and complete a table like the one belo

Start With...	Remove	Drawing	What's Left?	Sentence	Neutral Field Needed?
-5 and a neutral field	-3	+ + + + + ⊂ - - ⊃ - - - - - - -	-2	-5 - (-3) = -2	no
-5 and a neutral field	-8				
-5 and a neutral field	-4				
-5 and a neutral field	-7				
-5 and a neutral field	3				
-5 and a neutral field	5				
-5 and a neutral field	8				
-5 and a neutral field	4				

a)   Start with any number. When you subtract a negative number from the starting number, is the answer greater or less than the starting number?

b)   When you subtract a positive number from the starting number, is the answer greater or less than the starting number?

PR-28.   Use Guess and Check to solve this problem. Remember to write the solution in a complete sentence.

George has some erasers and coins in his pocket. He has seven more erasers than coins, and altogether he has 17 objects. How many of each item does he have?

Guess Number of Coins	Number of Erasers (Coins + 7)	Total Items	Check 17
10	(10) + 7 = 17		

PR-29.   Li, Debbie, and Mario were introduced to the Dart Booth. The numbers that each of them hit are given below. Write a sentence for each person that describes how to get their target number.

Numbers	Target Number	Solution In Words
Li's numbers: 2, 5, 6	16	
Debbie's numbers: 1, 2, 4	6	
Mario's numbers: 2, 5, 6	7	

PR-30.   I am thinking of two numbers. When they are multiplied, the product is 36. When the numbers are added, the sum is 15. What are the two numbers? Use a Guess and Check table to solve the problem.

Guess First Number	Second Number	Multiply the Two Numbers	Check 36
10	$15 - (10) = 5$	$(10) \cdot (5) = 50$	too high

PR-31.   Ashley has to paint $\frac{1}{2}$ of her bathroom ceiling. Alex has to paint $\frac{1}{4}$ of the school library ceiling.

$\frac{1}{2}$ of bathroom ceiling

a)   Who had to paint the larger fraction of a ceiling, Ashley or Alex?

b)   If the drawings at right are drawn accurately to scale, who painted more ceiling area?

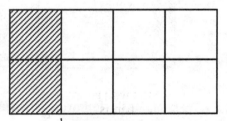

c)   Why do your answers from parts (a) and (b) disagree?

$\frac{1}{4}$ of library ceiling

PR-32.   Refer back to the Dart Board, the first problem in this chapter. In each part below, show how each player can hit his target number.

a)   Tom's darts landed on the numbers 3, 3, and 5. His target number is 14.

b)   Jerry's darts landed on 5, 6, and 7. His target number is 37.

PR-33.   A rectangular park is 150 yards long on one side and 125 yards on the other.

a)   If Deborah walks two times around the park, how far does she walk? Sketch a figure and show your work.

b)   If she wanted to walk 1,000,000 yards, how many times would she have to walk around the park?

PR-34.   The high temperatures for the last six Saturdays were 78°, 92°, 86°, 95°, 64°, and 89°.

a)   What is the mean high temperature for those Saturdays?

b)   What is the median high temperature for those Saturdays?

PR-35. Place your fraction-decimal-percent grid on top of the
boxes below. Think of your grid as 1 or one whole.
How much of the grid is shaded in each box? Put your
fraction, decimal, and percent in an arrow triangle like
the one at right.

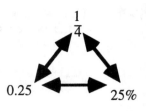

a)

b)

c)

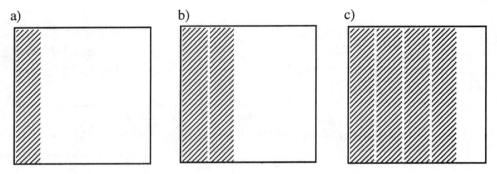

PR-36. Evaluate the following problem: $5 + 6 \cdot 2$.

Check with your partner to see if you both have the same answer. If you and your
partner do not agree, discuss what each of you did differently. Then write in words how
you arrived at your answer.

PR-37. Four students did the same problem and got different answers. Try to determine what
they did differently.

a) Albert evaluated $2 + 3 \cdot 4$ as 20. How did he get his result?

b) Bev evaluated $2 + 3 \cdot 4$ as 14. How did she get her result?

c) Kris evaluated $4 \cdot 3 + 2$ as 20. How did she get her result?

d) Darryl evaluated $4 \cdot 3 + 2$ as 14. How did he get his result?

PR-38. Circle the terms (parts) in the following expressions. Find the value of each expression.

Example:

$$2(8-7) + 4 \cdot 5 + 1 = \boxed{2(8-7)} + \boxed{4 \cdot 5} + \boxed{1}$$
$$= \boxed{2(1)} + \boxed{20} + \boxed{1}$$
$$= \boxed{2} + \boxed{20} + \boxed{1}$$
$$= \boxed{23}$$

a) $6 + 3 \cdot 4$

b) $6 \cdot 5 + 8 - (2 + 3)$

c) $2 \cdot 5 - 7 + 3 \cdot 3$

d) $(4 - 9) + 2 \cdot 3$

e) $9 \cdot 4 - 3(2 - 5) - (9 - 11)$

PR-39.   Explain in complete sentences how you can identify the terms (parts) in an expression. Share your answer with your team or partner.

PR-40.   In most of the following problems, a mistake was made. Write what mistake was made and finish the problem correctly. If no mistake was made, write, "No Mistake."

a) $3 + 2 \cdot 8$

$\boxed{3 + 2} \cdot \boxed{8}$

$5 \ \cdot \ 8$

40

b) $2 + 16 \div 2 \cdot 8$

$\boxed{2} + \boxed{16 \div 2 \cdot 8}$

$2 + 8 \cdot 8$

$10 \cdot 8$

80

c) $2 + 16 \div 2 \cdot 8$

$\boxed{2} + \boxed{16 \div 2 \cdot 8}$

$\boxed{2} + \boxed{8 \cdot 8}$

$2 + 64$

66

d) $2(16 - 2) + 2 \cdot 8$

$\boxed{2(16 - 2)} + \boxed{2 \cdot 8}$

$2 \cdot 14 + 16$

$2 \cdot 30$

60

PR-41.   Write an equation to represent each integer tile drawing.

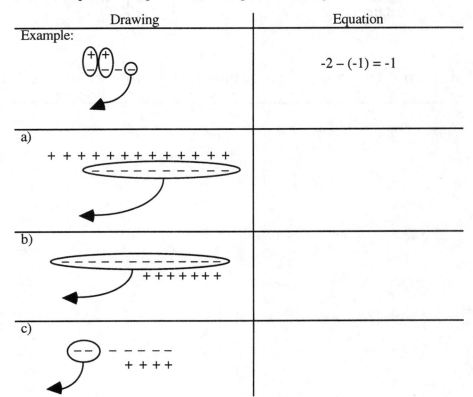

Drawing	Equation
Example:	$-2 - (-1) = -1$
a)	
b)	
c)	

PR-42.   Add the following.

   a)   3 + 10   b)   -6 + 13   c)   -3 + 2

PR-43.   In parts (a) and (b) below, you will compare problems PR-41 and PR-42.

   a)   Compare part (a) of problem PR-42 to part (a) of problem PR-41. How are the
         integers similar? How are they different? The operations are inverses. How do the
         answers compare?

   b)   Make the same comparison between parts (b) and (c) of both problems. Did you notic
         the same similarities and differences?

PR-44.   The student store wants to sell t-shirts. Morty's
          Shirts charges a $50 set-up fee to silkscreen blank
          t-shirts with the school logo. Each blank t-shirt
          costs $3. The bill for the t-shirts and screen printing
          is $131. How many t-shirts were ordered?

          Set up a Guess and Check table to solve this
          problem. Remember to write the answer in a
          complete sentence.

Guess How Many T-Shirts	Cost of Blank Shirts	Total Cost of Job (cost of blank shirts + setup fee)	Check $131
10	(10) · $3 = $30		

CHAPTER 3

PR-45.

ORDER OF OPERATIONS

An expression is organized into parts that are separated by addition (+) or subtraction (−) symbols <u>unless</u> the sum or difference is inside parentheses. Each part (a number, variable, product or quotient of numbers and variables) is called a **TERM**.

1. <u>Circle</u> the terms in the expression.

2. <u>Simplify</u> each term until it is one number by:
   - evaluating each exponential number.
   - performing each operation inside prentheses before doing any other operations in the term following the rule below.
   - multiplying and dividing from left to right.

3. Finally, <u>combine like terms</u> by adding and subtracting left to right.

Examples of a term include 4, $3x$, $-2y^4$, $\frac{3x}{7}$, $4(x + 3)$, and $5x(x - 2)^2$.

Example:

Simplify $3(6 - 3) + 4 \cdot 5^2 - 10$.

$\boxed{3(6-3)} + \boxed{4 \cdot 5^2} - \boxed{10}$

$\boxed{3(3)} + \boxed{4 \cdot 5 \cdot 5} - \boxed{10}$

$\boxed{9} + \boxed{4 \cdot 25} - \boxed{10}$

$\boxed{9} + \boxed{100} - \boxed{10}$

$109 - 10 = 99$

Make these notes in your Tool Kit to the right of the double-lined box.

a) Describe some mistakes students might make if they do not know the order of operations.

b) How will you help yourself remember the correct order of operations?

PR-46. In the expressions below, circle the terms and evaluate the expressions.

a) $2 \cdot 3 + 4 \cdot 5$

b) $2 \cdot (3 + 4) \cdot 5$

c) $2 \cdot 3 - 4 \cdot 5$

PR-47. Draw tile models and solve the problems in parts (a) through (i) below.

a) $8 - 12$

b) $-8 - (-12)$

c) $8 - (-12)$

d) $8 - 8$

e) $8 - (-8)$

f) $-8 - 8$

g) $8 + (-8)$

h) $8 + 8$

i) $-8 + (-8)$

j) Which of the answers in parts (a) through (i) are the same? Why?

PR-48. **Algebra Puzzles** Use the working backward "cover-up" method to solve these equations.

a) $8x + 3 = -21$

b) $-7 + 5x = -27$

c) $-32 = 12x + (-20)$

PR-49.   Work with your partner and use integer tiles to build the models represented by the first pair of expressions. Record both models and their equations on your paper. Then discuss and agree on your answers to the questions that follow.

a)   -5 – (-3) and -5 + 3

i)   Why does taking out a number of negatives give the same result as putting in the same number of positives?

ii)   Which expression is easier to compute without using tiles?

iii)   Do you think a subtraction problem can always be rewritten as an addition problem? Explain your reasoning.

b)   Repeat the process you completed for part (a) for 4 – 6 and 4 + (-6).

c)   Be prepared to discuss your results with the class.

PR-50.

┌───┐
│   **RULE FOR SUBTRACTING INTEGERS**   │
│   │
│ **Adding the opposite of the second number** gives the same answer as   │
│ subtracting it.   │
│   │
│ Step One: Change the subtraction sign to an addition sign.   │
│   │
│ Step Two: Change the sign of the integer you are subtracting.   │
│   │
│ Step Three: Use the integer rules for addition.   │
│   │
│ Example: $8 – (12) = 8 + (-12) = -4$.   │
└───┘

Make these notes in your Tool Kit to the right of the double-lined box.

Show how to do these subtraction problems: 34 – 13 and -34 – 13. Check with your partner or team to be sure that you did both problems correctly.

PR-51.   Simplify.

a)   -63 – (-17)   b)   -42 – 62   c)   -42 – (-62)

PR-52.   In Chapter 2 you used integer tiles to calculate products of integers. When you multiplied you were adding groups of positive or negative tiles. For example, if the problem was 3(2), you added 3 groups of 2. Copy and complete the table below.

	Problem	Sentence	Answer
a)	5(-3)	Add 5 groups of -3.	-15
b)	4(-4)	Add ____ groups of ____ .	
c)	6(-2)	Add ____ groups of ____ .	

PR-53. When we use integer tiles to multiply in a situation in which the first integer is negative, it becomes a repeated subtraction problem. Look at the problem (-4)(3).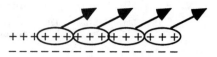

a) Draw a large neutral field. Circle and remove one group of +3. Do it again. Do it again. Do it one more time. What is left? How many times did you remove groups of +3?

b) Since multiplication shows a repeated process, the steps done in part (a) showed the problem (-4)(+3). The sentence describing the multiplication problem is "Remove four groups of positive three." What result did you get?

PR-54.

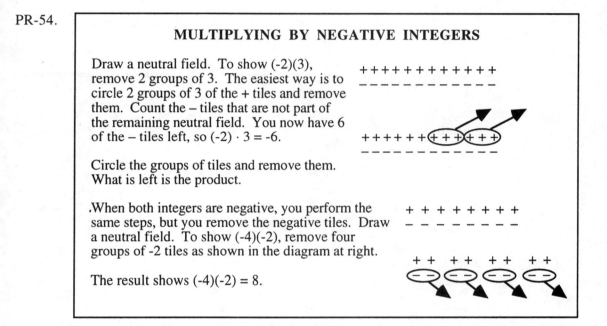

MULTIPLYING BY NEGATIVE INTEGERS

Draw a neutral field. To show (-2)(3), remove 2 groups of 3. The easiest way is to circle 2 groups of 3 of the + tiles and remove them. Count the – tiles that are not part of the remaining neutral field. You now have 6 of the – tiles left, so (-2) · 3 = -6.

Circle the groups of tiles and remove them. What is left is the product.

When both integers are negative, you perform the same steps, but you remove the negative tiles. Draw a neutral field. To show (-4)(-2), remove four groups of -2 tiles as shown in the diagram at right.

The result shows (-4)(-2) = 8.

Using integer tiles, draw a large neutral field and follow the same process as you did in the preceding problem.

a) Show (-5)(3). Complete the sentence: "Remove _____ groups of _____ . The result is _____ ."

b) Show (-7)(-2). Complete the sentence: "Remove _____ groups of _____. The result is _____ ."

PR-55. Multiply. Use an integer tile drawing if it helps you.

a) (-3)(4)   b) (-5)(-3)   c) (-2)(-3)

d) (-4)(5)   e) (-2)(8)   f) (-1)(-1)

PR-56. Work with your partner to make the following equations true. Use the numbers 3, 5, 8, and 9 exactly once in each equation.

a)

$$\square \cdot \square + (\square - \square) = 16$$

b)

$$\dfrac{\square}{\square} + \square \cdot \square = 43$$

PR-57. Place your fraction-decimal-percent grid on top of the boxes below. Think of your grid as 1 or one whole. How much of the grid is shaded in each box? Put your fraction, decimal, and percent in an arrow triangle like the one at right.

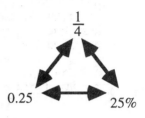

a)

b)

c)

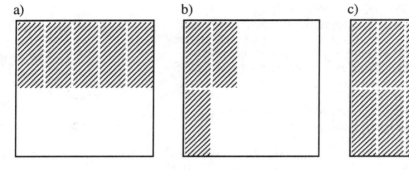

PR-58. Circle the terms and evaluate.

a) $2 \cdot (-11) + 13$

b) $-17 - 5 \cdot (-2)$

c) $14 - 2 \cdot (-2)$

d) $53 - (-7) \cdot 4$

e) $100 \cdot (-2) - (-10)$

f) $20 \cdot 7 + (-11) \cdot (-7)$

PR-59. Sohan built a rectangular pen for his sheep with an area of 242 square feet. He only had 66 feet of fencing to use. He wanted the length to be twice as long as the width. What were the dimensions of the pen? Draw a picture of the pen and label the length and width, then fill in the table and solve the problem using Guess and Check.

Guess Width of the Pen	Length of Pen	Area of Pen	Check

PR-60. Mrs. Poppington bought a new border to put around the bulletin board. One package contains 250 inches of border. The sides of the rectangular bulletin board are 72 inches and 36 inches. How much border will be <u>left</u> if it is used on all four sides of the bulletin board? Sketch the rectangle, label the sides, and show your work.

PR-61. Mr. Wong, the school principal, decided to play a game at the Dart Booth. His darts landed on 1, 4, 7, and 5, and the target number was 6. He won! To get 6, he subtracted 1 from 4 to get 3, and then he subtracted 5 from 7 to get 2. Finally, he multiplied 3 by 2.

a) Put parentheses in the expression $4 - 1 \cdot 7 - 5$ to get 6 as an answer.

b) What answer would you get if no parentheses were used?

PR-62. **Algebra Puzzles** Solve each equation.

a) $3x + 8 = -31$

b) $-7y - 15 = 34$

c) $-8w - 27 = 21$

d) $-4 + 9z = 50$

PR-63. Find the integers (whole numbers) between 1 and 50 with:

a) exactly three positive whole-number divisors.

b) exactly four positive whole-number divisors.

c) Write all of your answers to part (b) except for 8 and 27 as a product of primes. (Recall that a prime number is one that is only divisible by itself and 1. The first five primes are 2, 3, 5, 7, and 11.) What do you observe?

PR-64. Follow your teacher's directions to practice mental math. Write the strategy that you think is best, and explain why you think so.

PR-65. Simplify.

a) $-2 - (-3)$

b) $-2 + 3$

c) Why are the answers to (a) and (b) the same?

PR-66.   Copy and complete the following multiplication table.

	Drawing	Equation
Example:	+ + + + + + ⊖⊖⊖	$(-3)(-2) = 6$
a)	+ + + ⟩⟨ + + + ⟩ + + + – – – – – – – – –	
b)	+ + + + + + + + + + ⊖⊖⊖⊖⊖	

PR-67.   Multiply.

a) $(-4)(3)$ b) $(4)(-3)$

c) $(-3)(-4)$ d) $(3)(4)$

e)   Compare the integers in the answers to parts (a) through (d). How are they similar?
        How are they different?

f)   There is a rule about the sign of the product of two integers. Compare the signs of
        the answers in part (a) through (d) with the signs of the factors. What do you think
        the rule is?

PR-68.   It is time to play Tug-O-War II.

Tug-O-War II
A game for two people.

Mathematical Purpose: To practice integer addition and multiplication.

Object: To be the first to reach the space marked "Winner."

Materials: A resource page, a paper clip for the spinner, two game markers, and a pencil.

Scoring: The first person to land exactly on the "Winner" space wins the game.

How to Play the Game:

1. Start at zero.

2. Spin both spinners.
   - The "Groups of Steps" spinner determines how many times you may take your number of steps.
   - The "Number of Steps" spinner determines whether you move in a positive or negative direction and how many steps you will take.

3. Record your game on your paper in a chart like the one shown below.
   - Record your spins as a multiplication equation.
   - Record your new position as an addition equation.

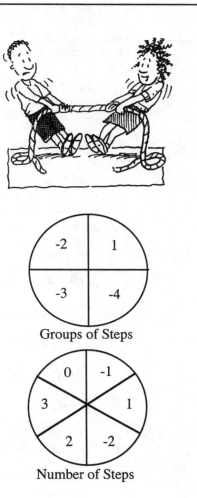

Groups of Steps

Number of Steps

Turn	Groups of Steps	Kind of Steps	Multiplication Problem	Your Position (addition problem)	Absolute Value (your distance from zero)
Example 1	-3	-2	$(-3)(-2) = 6$	$0 + 6 = 6$	$|6| = 6$
Example 2	-2	3	$(-2)(3) = -6$	$6 + (-6) = 0$	$|0| = 0$

4. If your move would make your marker go off the board on any play, you lose your turn.

Ending the Game: The game ends when one player lands <u>exactly</u> on the "Winner" space.

PR-69. Complete the Guess and Check table below. Write your answers in complete sentences.

There are three Ferris wheels at the fair. They all have the same number of seats, but one can hold three people in each seat and the other two can only hold two people in each seat. Altogether, 112 people can ride the Ferris wheels at one time. How many seats are on each Ferris wheel?

Guess # of Seats Per Ferris Wheel	People on Ferris Wheel #1	People on Ferris Wheel #2	People on Ferris Wheel #3	Total # of People	Check 112

PR-70. When Fred the Farmer got to the county fair, he needed to find pens for his horse, Blaze, his new two Holstein cows, Emily and Amanda, and his prize miniature pig, Petunia. Blaze was put in a rectangular horse box measuring 10 feet long and 6 feet wide. Emily and Amanda were put into a rectangular pen which was 12 feet long and 15 feet wide. Petunia had a small square pen 6 feet on a side.

a) Find the perimeter of Blaze's pen.

b) Find the perimeter of Emily and Amanda's pen.

c) Find the perimeter of Petunia's pen.

PR-71.

RULES FOR MULTIPLYING INTEGERS

1. If you multiply two integers with the **same sign**, the product is **positive**.

2. If you multiply two integers with **different signs**, the product is **negative**.

Examples: $(6)(-4) = -24$ $(-6)(-4) = 24$

Highlight the words "same sign," "positive," "different signs," and "negative" in your Tool Kit.

PR-72. Evaluate each expression.

a) $(-2) \cdot (-12) + 13$

b) $-17 + (-5) \cdot 6$

c) $14 - 13 \cdot (-2)$

d) $51 - (-7) \cdot 6$

e) $50 \cdot (-2) - (-12)$

f) $20 \cdot 7 + (-20) \cdot (-7)$

PR-73.   Simplify.

   a)   -5 – 3   b)   5 – 3

   c)   -5 + (-3)   d)   5 + (-3)

   e)   Which pairs of the answers in parts (a) through (d) are the same?

PR-74.   A triangular flower bed needs a border. The sides are 7 feet, 6 feet, and 9 feet.

   a)   How many feet of border should be purchased? Make a sketch and show your
         work.

   b)   If borders cost $8.75 per yard (and only whole numbers of yards can be purchased),
         how much would the border cost?

PR-75.   Use the numbers 2, 6, and 8 to make the equations true in part (a), (b), and (c).

   a) 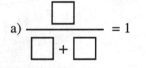   b) $\square + \square \cdot \square = 22$

                                             In part (d) use the numbers 3, 5, 8, and 9
                                             to get 10.

   c) $(\square - \square) \cdot \square = 32$ d)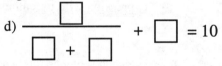

PR-76.   Find each of the following sums.

   a) $|7| + |14|$ b) $|-16| + |-18|$

   c) $|-14| + |27|$ d) $|44| + |-12|$

PR-77.   **Algebra Puzzles**   Solve each equation.

   a) $13 – 43x = 13$ b) $55y – 99 = -99$

   c) $419w + 419 = 0$ d) $10 – 3z = 37$

PR-78. Here we investigate how inserting parentheses can change the value of an expression. Note that $(2 + 3) \cdot 4 + 5$ is different from $2 + 3 \cdot (4 + 5)$.

a) Use the order of operations to evaluate $6 \cdot 5 - 2 \cdot 3$ correctly.

b) Do these parentheses change the value of the expression? $(6 \cdot 5) - (2 \cdot 3)$

c) Now add parentheses to $6 \cdot 5 - 2 \cdot 3$ in different ways to get as many different values as you can.

PR-79. Lori's darts landed on the numbers 7, 4, 4, and 5. Use parentheses, multiplication, addition, and subtraction to write an equation that gives a target number of 39.

PR-80. At the Dart Booth, Tatiana's darts landed on the numbers 2, 3, 6, and 8. We can get her target number, 24, by first subtracting 2 from 8 to get 6. Next we can multiply the 6 by 3 to get 18. Then we can add the 6 to the 18 to get 24. Written as an equation, the sum would be $3 (8 - 2) + 6 = 24$.

a) Tatiana said, "I got 24. It is 2 times 8 plus 6 – 2." Write this expression with parentheses so Tatiana is correct.

b) Verna Ray said, "You can also get 24 as 6 times 8 minus 2 times 2." Write this expression with parentheses so Verna Ray is correct.

PR-81. Translate each sentence into a correct numerical equation.

a) Four times two times three minus four equals eight.

b) Seven minus three times six minus one equals twenty.

c) One million plus ten thousand times zero equals zero.

PR-82. Create a table to organize a set of points which follow the rule $y = 2x - 1$. Graph the ordered pairs on a coordinate grid.

PR-83. Circle the terms (parts), then find the value of each expression below.

a) $4 + 7 \cdot 2$

b) $(-3)(4 - 7) + 9$

c) $6 \cdot 8 - 3(5 - 8)$

d) $7 - 6 \cdot 5 - 4(5 - 8)$

PR-84. Draw a number line and label the intervals using a scale that will allow you to place the following list of numbers as points on the number line: $-5\frac{1}{2}$, -2, $4\frac{3}{4}$, 6, -1, $\frac{3}{2}$, and -0.5.

PR-85. Stefano's darts landed on the numbers 7, 5, 6, and 3. He can get his target number of 75 by writing the equation $(7 + 5) \cdot 6 + 3 = 75$.

a) Stefano decided to play again and his darts landed on 2, 6, 6, and 4. Use addition, subtraction, multiplication, division and parentheses to get the target numbers of 16, 24, and 12. Record your equations.

b) Continue, using 2, 6, 6, and 4, and combine the numbers to equal three different target numbers. Write an equation for each target number.

PR-86. Place your fraction-decimal-percent grid on top of the boxes below. Think of your grid as 1 or one whole. How much of the grid is shaded in each box? Put your fraction, decimal, and percent in an arrow triangle like the one at right.

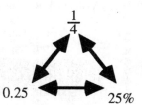

a)   b)   c)

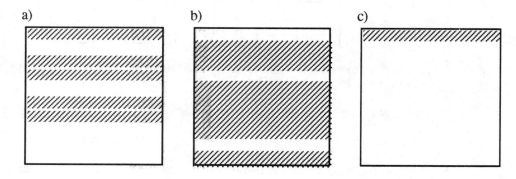

PR-87. Find the sum or difference.

a) $|50| + |-10|$ b) $|-45| + |16|$

c) $|-14| + |27|$ d) $|44| - |-12|$

PR-88.   Ms. Bains had eight students who did an extra credit assignment to raise their grades. The scores on the assignment were 45, 100, 100, 67, 98, 33, 60, and 100. Make a stem and-leaf plot of these data. Find the median and mode.

PR-89.   **Algebra Puzzles** Solve each equation.

   a) $15x + 83 = -7$ b) $-26 + 20w = -106$

PR-90.   **County Fair Pig Race** The big event has finally arrived! You and your partner have entered a pig in the annual County Fair Pig Race. You will be racing your pig along a 43-yard track, and your pig will be competing against your classmates' pigs. Get a resource page from your teacher and look at the track for the race.

   The race is very simple. Just follow the rules below to go from the pigsty to the winner's circle. You will need two resource pages and pencils.

   1.   Your teacher will roll four dice. Write the number of each die in a space on the resource page.

         If your teacher were to roll a 5, 3, 4, and another 5, your resource page would look similar to this:

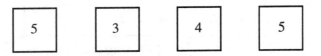

| 5 | 3 | 4 | 5 |

   2.   You must use all four numbers to try and hit one of the three target numbers listed in the table below.

   3.   You may use any of the arithmetic operations (+, −, x, and ÷) and parentheses.

   4.   You may only use one combination for any set of four numbers.

   5.   When you have a solution in a round, you must record the equation on your resource page below the boxes for that round.

   6.   Your pig will move forward along the track every time you hit a target.

   7.   Your teacher will roll a new set of numbers every few minutes.

   8.   You may only hit a target once per set of numbers.

   9.   At the end of the race, your equations must be checked and approved by the teacher to win. If you have any incorrect equations, you may be disqualified.

                        >>Problem continues on the next page.>>

Target Number	Distance Your Pig Can Move	Equation Used
51	8 yards	
34	7 yards	
21	5 yards	
1	3 yards	
any prime number	2 yards	
any other number	1 yard	

PR-91.   Add or subtract each expression.

a) $2 - 4$ b) $2 - (-4)$ c) $2 + (-4)$ d) $2 + 4$

PR-92.   Circle the terms (parts), then find the value of each expression below.

a) $7 + 6 \cdot 3$ b) $2(8 - 3) + 6$

c) $4 \cdot 2 - 2(3 - 7)$ d) $5 + 2 \cdot 3 - 3(4 - 5)$

PR-93.   As you can tell from the examples of modified number lines, not all number lines increase by one unit from mark to mark. Fill in the missing numbers on the number lines below.

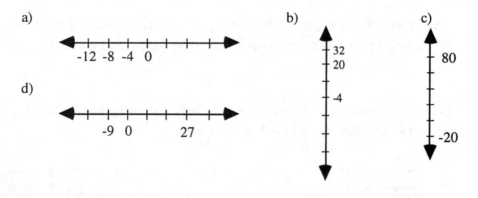

a)

-12 -8 -4 0

b)

32
20

-4

c)

80

-20

d)

-9 0   27

PR-94.   **Mental Math** Perform the following calculations in your head without a pencil or paper. Be prepared to explain your method.

a) $100 \cdot \$0.30$ b) $100 \cdot \$0.50$ c) $100 \cdot \$0.60$

PR-95. Use a Guess and Check table to solve this problem. Remember to label sections of the table and write your answer in a sentence.

Carrie works at the lemonade stand at the fair. She sold 235 glasses of lemonade. She sold four times as many large glasses as small ones. How many of each size did she sell?

Guess # small	# Large	Total Glasses	Check _____

PR-96. Use 1, 3, 5, and 6 exactly once per equation to make the following equations true.

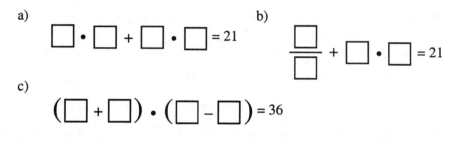

a)
$$\square \cdot \square + \square \cdot \square = 21$$

b)
$$\frac{\square}{\square} + \square \cdot \square = 21$$

c)
$$(\square + \square) \cdot (\square - \square) = 36$$

PR-97. Charlie's sister, a third-grader, asked him to show her how to add $\frac{3}{4} + \frac{3}{4}$. Help Charlie by drawing a picture and explaining clearly so the third-grader will understand.

PR-98. Paris drew figure (i) to represent $\frac{3}{4} + \frac{3}{4}$. Madison drew figure (ii). Which picture do you think illustrates the problem better and why?

i)

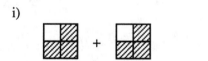

ii)

PR-99. Write each number five different ways. For example, $\frac{1}{2}$ could be written $\frac{50}{100}$.

a) $\frac{1}{2}$

b) $\frac{2}{3}$

c)   1 whole

PR-100. **Algebra Puzzles** Solve these equations. Show the steps. A calculator will help. Solutions will be approximations.

a)   788x + 837 = 2433   b)   419x + 332 = -1944

PR-101. **Chapter Summary**

It is time to summarize and review what you have learned in this chapter. In teams or with a partner, you will be making a mobile. You may choose examples from the following list of problems for each topic:

- Guess and Check: PR-2, 3, 4, 5, 28, and 44

- Multiplication of integers: PR-55, 67, and 71

- Subtraction of integers: PR-14, 15, 16, 20, and 47

- Order of operations: PR-38, 46, 58, 72, and 83

- Equivalent fractions, decimals, and percents: PR-25, 26, 35, 57, and 86

Your team should divide the work in order to complete the mobile in one class period. For each topic, the mobile must have a concept label and a sample problem. See the example at right.

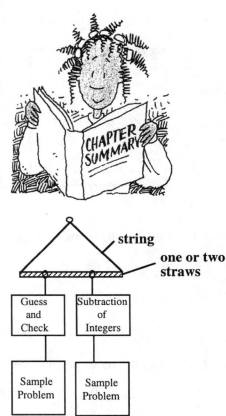

PR-102. Lindsey, Stephanie, and Grant entered quilts they made at the fair. Lindsey took 8 hours longer than her sister, Stephanie, to make her quilt. Grant took the same amount of time as Lindsey and Stephanie combined. Altogether the three quilts required 168 hours to make. How long did Grant take to make his prize-winning quilt?

Guess Stephanie's Hours	

PR-103. Place your fraction-decimal-percent grid on top of the boxes below. Think of your grid as 1 or one whole. How much of the grid is shaded in each box? Put your fraction, decimal, and percent in an arrow triangle like the one at right.

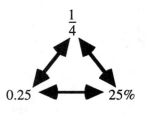

a)   b)   c)

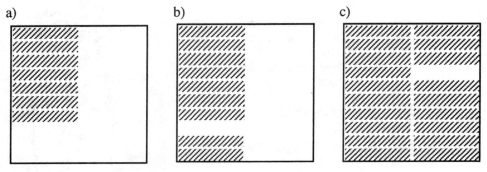

PR-104. Evaluate the following expressions:

a) $-3 + 7 \cdot 2$

b) $-3 \cdot 7 + (-2)$

c) $-5 \cdot 4 + (-2) \cdot (-4)$

d) $-3 + 7 + (-2)(-2\frac{1}{2})$

e) $45 - (-9) + (-8)(1\frac{1}{2})$

f) $-3 - (-2(3 + 63 \div 9))$

PR-105. Calculate these products and explore the rules for products of 3 or more numbers.

a) $(2)(3)(4)$

b) $(-2)(3)(4)$

c) $(-2)(-3)(4)$

d) $(-2)(-3)(-4)$

e) $(2)(3)(4)(5)$

f) $(-2)(-3)(4)(5)$

g) $(-2)(3)(4)(5)$

h) $(-2)(-3)(-4)(5)$

i) $(-2)(-3)(-4)(-5)$

j)   Write a conjecture (a guess based on a pattern) about how to determine if a product is positive or negative by counting the number of negative integers in the product.

PR-106. In most of the following problems a mistake was made. Identify and describe what mistake was made and finish the problem correctly. If no mistake was made, write "No mistake."

a)

$(3 + 2) \cdot 8$

$\boxed{(3) + (2)} \cdot 8$

$3 + 16$

19

b)

$2 + (72 \div 12 - 6)$

$(2) + \boxed{(72 \div 12 - 6)}$

$2 + 72 \div 6$

$2 + 12$

18

c)

$2 + 16 \div 2 \cdot 8$

$18 \div 2 \cdot 8$

$9 \cdot 8$

72

d)

$2(16 - 2) + 2 \cdot 8$

$\boxed{2(16 - 2)} + \boxed{2 \cdot 8}$

$\boxed{2 \cdot 14} + \boxed{16}$

$28 + 16$

44

PR-107. **Algebra Puzzles** Solve each equation. Show the steps. A calculator will help.

a) $\frac{x}{97} + 1042 = 9840$

b) $\frac{x}{64} - 398 = -465$

PR-108. There is a game at the fair in which you toss balls into bowls to win fish. There are 52 bowls. The larger bowls contain five fish, and the smaller ones contain three fish. If there are 202 fish total, how many bowls of each size are there?

Guess Number of Small Bowls	

PR-109.   After spending a hot afternoon walking through
          the fair booths, Leo and Stefano decided to buy
          refreshments from the Fruit and Smoothies
          Stand. Fruit kabobs cost $1.75 each and
          smoothies cost $2.50 each.

   a)   Leo ordered two fruit kabobs and one
        smoothie. How much did he spend?

   b)   Stefano ordered three fruit kabobs and four
        smoothies. How much did he spend?

   c)   Use f to represent the number of fruit
        kabobs and s to represent the number
        of smoothies. Write an expression to represent the <u>total</u> <u>cost</u> for any number of fruit
        kabobs and any number of smoothies.

PR-110.   Mr. Wong's school was going to go to the State Fair. He needed to get buses for the
          students. Each bus holds 50 students. Tatiana and Krista made graphs to show the
          number of children that could be carried on the buses. Tatiana made graph A, and Krista
          made graph B. Which graph is correct and why?

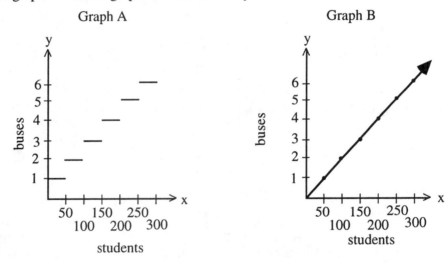

PR-111.   **What We Have Done in This Chapter**

          Below is a list of the Tool Kit entries from this chapter.

          • PR-5   Solving Problems with Guess and Check Tables
          • PR-45   Order of Operations
          • PR-50   Rule for Subtracting Integers
          • PR-71   Rules for Multiplying Integers

          Review all the entries and read the notes you made in your
          Tool Kit. Make a list of any questions, terms, or notes you

          you do not understand. Ask your partner or study team members for help. If anything is
          still unclear, ask your teacher.

Mrs. Poppington Sees The World

Chapter 4

Chapter 4
Mrs. Poppington Sees The World: **AREA and MULTIPLICATION**

This chapter develops some of the ideas from a branch of mathematics known as geometry. Throughout the chapter you will practice finding the area of shapes found on flags from around the world. The problem solving strategy called "solving subproblems" will be helpful to find the area of irregular shapes. In addition, you will use a geometric model to help understand multiplication of two- and three-digit numbers. You will continue solving word problems using Guess and Check tables.

In this chapter you will have the opportunity to:

- learn some of the vocabulary of geometry related to lines, angles, and polygons.

- develop and use formulas to find the areas of rectangles, parallelograms, triangles, and trapezoids.

- identify subproblems to find areas of more complicated figures and to solve other mathematical problems.

- explore the relationship between area and multiplication, then use an area model to identify subproblems when multiplying two- and three-digit numbers.

Read the problem below. What you learn over the next few days will enable you to solve it.

MP-0.   Mrs. Poppington has invited visitors from some of the countries she has visited to come and speak to her class. To make the visitors feel welcome, your team has been asked to create a quilt containing the flag for each visitor's country. By the end of the chapter, you will be able to determine how much material of each color you will need to make flags like those shown at right.

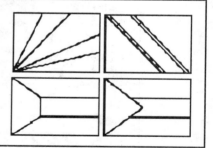

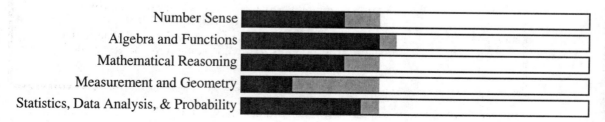

Number Sense

Algebra and Functions

Mathematical Reasoning

Measurement and Geometry

Statistics, Data Analysis, & Probability

Chapter 4
Mrs. Poppington Sees The World: **AREA and MULTIPLICATION**

MP-1.

These are the vocabulary words you practiced today:

Angles

acute angle	An angle with measure greater than 0° and less than 90°.
right angle	An angle that measures 90°.
obtuse angle	An angle with measure greater than 90° and less than 180°.
vertical angles	The opposite angles where two lines meet.

Triangles

acute triangle	A triangle in which all three angle measures are less than 90°.
right triangle	A triangle in which one angle is a right angle (measures 90°).
obtuse triangle	A triangle with an obtuse angle (greater than 90°).
scalene triangle	A triangle with no equal side lengths.
isosceles triangle	A triangle with two or more sides of equal length.
equilateral triangle	A triangle with all side lengths equal.

Quadrilaterals

trapezoid	A quadrilateral with one pair of parallel sides.
parallelogram	A quadrilateral with both pairs of opposite sides parallel.
rectangle	A quadrilateral with four right (90°) angles.
rhombus	A quadrilateral with all four sides of equal length.
square	A special rectangle with all sides of equal length.

Polygons

polygon	A two-dimensional closed figure of straight line segments (called edges or sides) connected end to end.
regular polygon	A polygon in which all side lengths are equal and all angle measures are equal.
quadrilateral	A polygon with four sides.
pentagon	A polygon with five sides.
hexagon	A polygon with six sides.
octagon	A polygon with eight sides.
vertex	The point where two consecutive sides of a polygon meet.
diagonal	A line segment that connects two vertices of a polygon and is not a side.

Other terms

circle	A set of points at a fixed distance (radius) from a point (center).
parallel lines	Two straight lines on a two-dimensional plane that do not intersect no matter how far they are extended.
perpendicular lines	Two lines on a flat surface which make a right angle when they meet.
line segment	The part of a line between two points.
ray	Part of a line that starts at a point on the line and contains all the points on the line that are on one side of the starting point.
base	A special side of a polygon used to compute area. (See examples in problems MP-16, MP-43, and MP-55).
height	In a triangle, parallelogram, or trapezoid, the perpendicular distance from a vertex to the line containing the "opposite" side (possibly extended).

In your Tool Kit highlight any term that was new to you today.

MP-2. On a geoboard paper resource page, sketch an example of each of the following terms.

a) right triangle   b) square   c) trapezoid   d) obtuse triangle
e) pentagon   f) diagonal   g) scalene triangle   h) base
i) vertical angles   j) quadrilateral   k) isosceles triangle   l) parallelogram
m) parallel lines   n) acute triangle   o) octagon   p) obtuse angle

MP-3. One side of a rectangle is 15 centimeters longer than the other side. The perimeter of the rectangle is 94 centimeters. What is the width of the rectangle? Use a Guess and Check table and remember to answer with a complete sentence.

Guess	Length	Perimeter	Check

MP-4. When Mrs. Poppington was in England, she learned that a fortnight is one way to measure time. Since she is a math teacher, she decided to create a puzzle for her class to solve. Start with 23, subtract the number of days in a fortnight, multiply the total by five, then subtract eight. The answer is 37. How many days are in a fortnight? Use a Guess and Check table and remember to answer with a complete sentence.

Guess	Subtract from 23	Multiply	Subtract	Check

MP-5. Use what you know about the order of operations to simplify the following expressions.

a) $9 + 12 \cdot (-3)$ b) $(9 + 12) \div 3$ c) $(9.6 + 4.4) \div (3 + 4)$

MP-6. Study your polygon vocabulary from problem MP-1 for five minutes. Cover up each definition and see whether you can say the definition to yourself. If you can, cover each vocabulary word and see if you can state the word when you know the definition. When you are done, write this statement next to this problem number: "I studied my polygon vocabulary for five minutes."

MP-7. **Algebra Puzzles** Decide which number belongs in place of the variable to make the equation true. Your solutions in parts (a) through (c) should be fractions.

a) $2x - 1 = 0$ b) $3x - 1 = 0$

c) $4x - 1 = 0$ d) $5x = 0$

MP-8. Jonathan claims that $13 - 2 \cdot 5 = 55$. Explain why he is wrong.

MP-9. Answer the following questions.

a) How many $\frac{1}{8}$ s are in 1? b) How many $\frac{1}{3}$ s are in 1?

c) How many $\frac{1}{3}$ s are in 3? d) How many $\frac{1}{5}$ s are in 2?

e) How many $\frac{3}{4}$ s are in $2\frac{1}{4}$? f) Explain your reasoning for your answer in part (e).

MP-10. Today your teacher will give you and your partner some geometry vocabulary flash cards to practice the words you reviewed on the geoboard earlier. Write the fraction of the cards that you got correct next to the problem number on your paper and change this fraction to a percent.

MP-11. Find the area of each of the figures below in square units. Show your work.

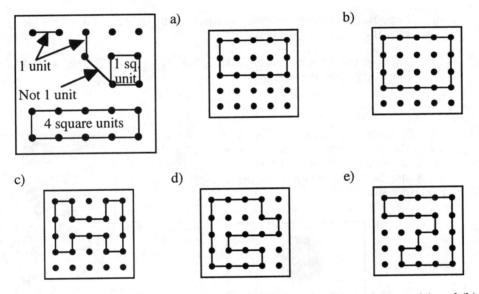

f) Use four different vocabulary words to name the figures in parts (a) and (b) accurately.

MP-12. Study the figures in parts (a) and (b) of the previous problem. Focus on the number of rows and the number of square units in each row.

a) How many rows of 4 square units are in the rectangle of part (a) above? What is the area?

b) How many rows of 4 square units are in the rectangle of part (b) above? What is the area?

c) Suppose a rectangle had 60 rows of 4 square units. What would the area be? How did you solve the problem?

MP-13.   Now we will connect what we have been doing with dot paper to finding areas of rectangles on plain paper. Below is a rectangle 3 units high and 4 units wide.

a)   How many square units are in the rectangle shown at right?

b)   Since you have rows of four squares, what is another way in which you might find the area?

c)   Is there a faster way to find the area of a rectangle than simply counting squares? Discuss this with your partner.

d)   Suppose you have a rectangle with nine rows. Each row has 6 square units. Find the area of this rectangle without drawing a picture. Explain how you got your answer.

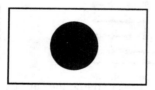

MP-14.   We want to use the same idea as in the previous problem to find the areas of other rectangles.

a)   Suppose you have a rectangle that is 40 units high and 10 units wide. Find the area of this rectangle.

b)   Suppose you have a rectangle that is 5 units high and 200 units wide. Find the area of this rectangle.

MP-15.   Mrs. Poppington puts flag stickers on her suitcase when she visits various countries. Below is the flag of Japan, which is often referred to as the Empire of the Rising Sun. The red circle on the flag represents the rising sun.

List at least five geometric vocabulary words that can be used to describe the flag.

MP-16.

┌───┐
│   │
│   **AREA OF A RECTANGLE**   │
│   │
│   Area of a Rectangle = (base) · (height)   │
│   │
│   **A = b · h**   │
│   │
│   Area = base · height   │
│   3   = 4 · 3   │
│   height   = 12   │
│   4   │
│   base   │
│   │
└───┘

Make these notes in your Tool Kit to the right of the double-lined box.

If a rectangle has a base of 6 and a height of 9, show how to find the area. Check your work with your partner or team to be sure it is correct.

MP-17.   Find the area of each rectangle below. Remember to label your answer with the appropriate units.

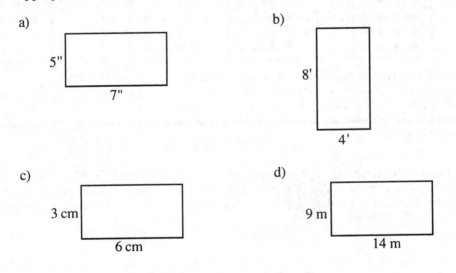

a)

5"

7"

b)

8'

4'

c)

3 cm

6 cm

d)

9 m

14 m

MP-18. When Mrs. Poppington went to Eastern Europe and visited Ukraine, she got a sticker that looks like the flag at right. The flag is cut into two equal parts, one blue and one yellow.

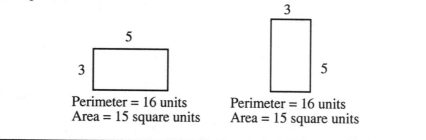

Blue

Yellow

a) List at least five geometric vocabulary terms that apply to this flag.

b) If the flag is $13\frac{1}{2}$ by 17 inches, how much of the area is yellow?

MP-19. Find the area of each figure.

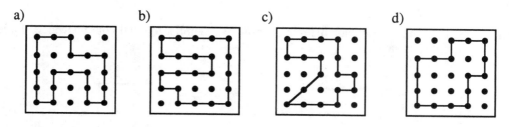

a)   b)   c)   d)

MP-20.

CONGRUENCE

Figures that have exactly the same size and shape are called **CONGRUENT**. When one congruent figure is placed on top of the other, all sides and angles match. (One figure may have to be rotated or flipped.) Congruent figures have the same area and perimeter.

3

5

3

5

Perimeter = 16 units
Area = 15 square units

Perimeter = 16 units
Area = 15 square units

Make these notes in your Tool Kit to the right of the double-lined box.

Draw two shapes that are congruent and make one tilted in relation to the other.

MP-21.   Do the following pairs of shapes <u>appear</u> to be congruent? If not, why not?

a)

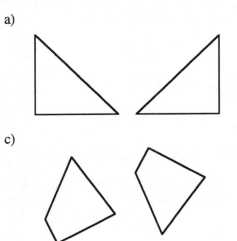

b)

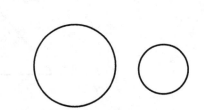

c)

d)   Two shapes have the same area and
different perimeters. Are the shapes
congruent? Explain why or why not.

MP-22.   Now that we have started a new chapter, it is
time for you to organize your binder.

a)   Put the work from the last chapter in order
and keep it in a separate folder.

b)   When this is completed, write, "I have
organized my binder."

MP-23.   Today your teacher will give you and your partner some geometry vocabulary flash cards
to practice the words you reviewed on the geoboard earlier. Write the fraction of the
cards that you got correct next to the problem number on your paper and change this
fraction to a percent.

MP-24.   For each of the following questions, draw the picture on grid, graph, or dot paper.

a)   Draw a rectangle that is not a square.

b)   Draw a parallelogram that is not a rectangle.

c)   Draw a trapezoid with exactly two right angles.

d)   Draw a right isosceles triangle.

e)   Draw a hexagon with exactly three right angles.

f)   Draw a quadrilateral in which the diagonals are equal in length.

MP-25.   Carefully cut out the first parallelogram from the resource page your teacher gives you.

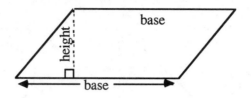

a)   Label the bases and the height.

b)   Use a ruler to measure the base and height in centimeters. Label their lengths.

c)   Cut along the height to separate the triangle from the rest of the figure. Then move the triangle to the right side of the figure, as shown below. Paste, glue, or tape the pieces in your notebook.

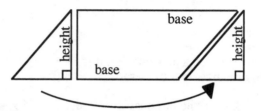

d)   What is the shape of the new figure?

e)   Find the area of the new rectangle.

f)   Explain why the rectangle and the parallelogram have the same area.

MP-26.

BASE AND HEIGHT OF A PARALLELOGRAM

Any side of a parallelogram can be its **BASE**. The **HEIGHT** of the parallelogram is the length of a perpendicular line segment from a vertex (or any other point on the side opposite the base) to the base or an extension of the base.

Make these notes in your Tool Kit to the right of the double-lined box.

Draw a parallelogram. Label the base and height. Be sure that the height makes a right angle with the base. Check your work with your partner or team to be sure that your example is correct.

MP-27.   A way that many people like to think about the
         height and base of a parallelogram is to think of
         the side of the parallelogram that sits on the
         horizontal (flat) ground as its BASE. Then the
         HEIGHT of the parallelogram is the distance a
         bowling ball would drop from a vertex (or any
         other point on the side opposite the base) straight
         down to the ground.

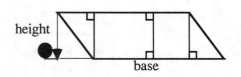

a)   Look at the rectangles (dotted lines) and parallelograms (solid lines) in parts (i)
     through (vi) below and label the base and height for each of these figures on your
     resource page.

b)   For each parallelogram, shade the triangle that could be moved to convert the
     parallelogram to a rectangle.

c)   Find the area of each rectangle.

d)   Find the area of each parallelogram.

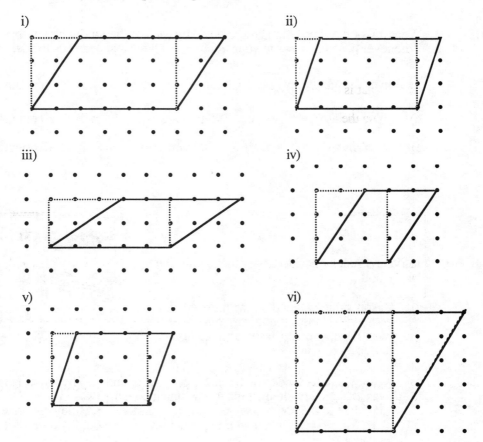

i)

ii)

iii)

iv)

v)

vi)

Mrs. Poppington Sees the World: Area and Multiplication   109

MP-28.   Find the area of each parallelogram below.

a)

b)

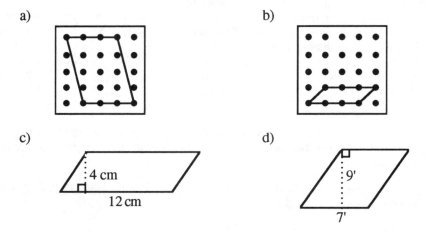

c)

4 cm

12 cm

d)

9'

7'

e)   What part of each parallelogram is represented by the vertical dotted line?

MP-29.   What fraction of one hour is represented by each of the following numbers of minutes? Whenever possible, rewrite your fraction using halves, quarters, thirds, or sixths.

Example: 30 minutes $= \frac{30}{60}$ or $\frac{1}{2}$ hour.

a)   15 minutes

b)   10 minutes   c)   45 minutes   d)   20 minutes

e)   40 minutes   f)   17 minutes   g)   90 minutes

MP-30.   Jason and Ashley decided to try their skills at the Dart Booth.

a)   Jason's darts landed on the numbers 2, 8, 7, and 5. If the winning target number was 10, how could Jason arrange his numbers to win?

b)   Ashley's darts landed on the numbers 1, 3, 0, and 7. The winning target number was 28. Ashley claimed that the winning equation was $3 + 1 \cdot 7 + 0 = 28$. The attendant in the booth disagreed and refused to give Ashley the prize. Why is $3 + 1 \cdot 7 + 0 = 28$ not a winning equation? How could you make it a winning equation?

MP-31. **Algebra Puzzles** Determine which number belongs in place of the variable to make the equation true.

    a) $1 - 2x = 0$ b) $1 - 3x = 0$

    c) $1 - 4x = 0$ d) $0 = 5x$

MP-32. Use your fraction-decimal-percent grid. Write a sentence that lists equivalent expressions for the shaded area in each box. Be sure to name at least one fraction, one decimal, and one percent.

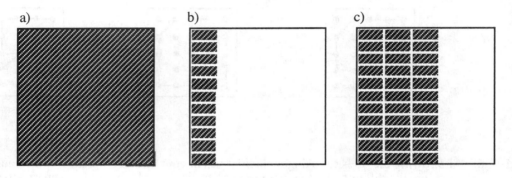

a)   b)   c)

MP-33. You know an algebraic rule such as $y = \frac{x}{2}$ is a formula for obtaining y values when you know the x values. A table is a good way to organize the coordinate points that create this algebraic pattern.

    a)   Create a table to organize a set of points which follow the rule $y = 3x + 1$.

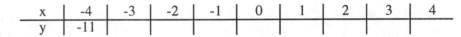

x	-4	-3	-2	-1	0	1	2	3	4
y	-11								

    b)   Plot the ordered pairs you have in your table on a coordinate grid.

MP-34. Today your teacher will give you and your partner some geometry vocabulary flash cards to practice the words you reviewed on the geoboard earlier. Write the fraction of the cards that you got correct next to the problem number on your paper and change this fraction to a percent.

MP-35.   **Area Problems** Your teacher will show you the six shapes below. With your partner, discuss the area of each shape, and then write down its area.

a)   b)   c)

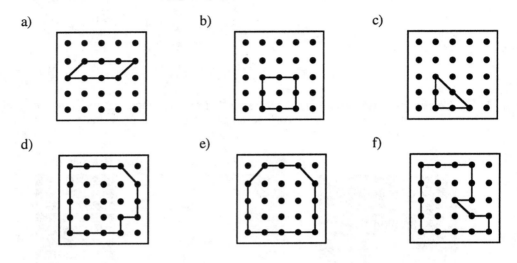

d)   e)   f)

MP-36.   Following the rules for using manipulatives in your classroom, take a few minutes to explore the different pieces your teacher has distributed to you. Be prepared to share what you know about base ten blocks.

a)   What does each piece represent?

b)   How many of each block does it take to make the next larger block?

c)   Using the least number of blocks, build the numbers 30, 45, and 132. Then sketch and label each number on your paper.

MP-37.   During the next few days we will be using base ten blocks to model multiplication problems. Begin by using the blocks to build a rectangle with a base of 3 units and a height of 7 units.

a)   Sketch your model.

b)   What is the area of the rectangle you built? Write the related problem with the answer.

MP-38.   With your teacher, you will build models of multiplication which will show why the standard technique works and which will also be useful in algebra. To begin, we give a model for multiplying $3 \cdot 12$. You should use your base ten blocks to copy what your teacher does. Then answer the questions.

What to do:

i)   Use three base ten "longs" to build a model of $3 \cdot 10$.

ii)   Use six base ten cubes to build a model of $3 \cdot 2$.

iii)   Put your two sets of blocks together to show a model of $3 \cdot (10 + 2)$ or $3 \cdot 12$.

a)   What are the dimensions of the rectangle you have just constructed?

b)   What is the area of this rectangle?

c)   Explain how your work shows that $3 \cdot 12 = 3(10 + 2) = 3 \cdot 10 + 3 \cdot 2$.

MP-39.   Use base ten blocks to build $10 \cdot 10$. Sketch your result. What is the smallest number of blocks you can use to represent this area? This block is called a flat.

MP-40.   Build a rectangle that models $16 \cdot 14$, which you can think of as $(10 + 6) \cdot (10 + 4)$.

a)   Make a sketch on your paper as shown at right. Separate the rectangle into four rectangular regions.

b)   These rectangular regions are the subproblems for the multiplication problem. Copy these subproblems near your drawing.

$\left.\begin{array}{l}10(10) \\ 10(4)\end{array}\right\rangle\ 10(14)$
$\left.\begin{array}{l}6(10) \\ 6(4)\end{array}\right\rangle\ 6(14)$

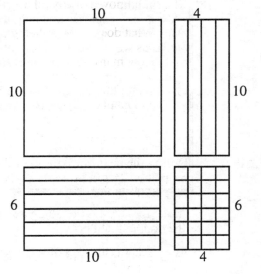

c)   Explain why the top two regions represent $10 \cdot 14$.

d)   Explain why the bottom two regions represent $6 \cdot 14$.

e)   Explain why all the regions together represent $16 \cdot 14$.

f)   Now do the problem with the traditional multiplication algorithm (method) and record it on your paper next to the subproblems you just finished. Do the answers agree?

MP-41.   Build the rectangle that models 14 · 12, which means (10 + 4) · (10 + 2). Make a sketch
on your paper.

a)   Separate the rectangle into four regions
and write the subproblems that represent
the four areas. Add them to find the total
area.

b)   Multiply 14 · 12. Check to see that the
answers agree.

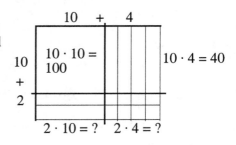

MP-42.   Build the rectangular model of 13 · 14. Include a sketch and label the dimensions. Show
the subproblems you use to find the total area. Multiply 13 · 14. Check to see that your
answers agree.

MP-43.

┌───┐
║   **AREA OF A PARALLELOGRAM**   ║
║   ║
║   To find the area of a parallelogram, the formula is **Area = base · height** or ║
║   **A = b · h**. The base and height are perpendicular to each other. **Rectangles** and ║
║   **squares** are special parallelograms, so you can use the same formula to find their ║
║   areas as well. We use the symbols > and >> to show pairs of parallel sides. ║
║   ║
║   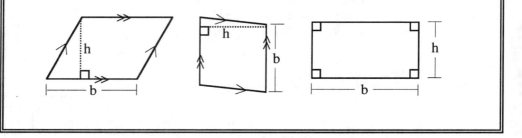   ║
└───┘

Make these notes including a sketch of the parallelograms in your Tool Kit to the right of
the double-lined box.

a)   Find the area of the parallelogram at right.

b)   Did you use all three numbers? Why or why not?

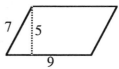

MP-44.   Compute the value of each expression.

a) $3 + 4 \cdot 5$

b) $21 - 6 \cdot 3 + 2(13 - 8)$

c) $7 \cdot 8 - 26$

d) $9 \cdot 5 + 4(2 + (-3)) + 2 \cdot 9$

e) $2 \cdot 3 + 5 - (8 - 6)$

f) $8 \cdot 2 + 3 \cdot (-2) - 5 \cdot 2$

MP-45.   What fraction of one dollar is represented by each of the following sets of coins?

Example: one quarter = $\frac{25}{100}$ = $\frac{1}{4}$ a)   three dimes

b)   eight nickels   c)   23 pennies

d)   five quarters   e)   nine dimes

f)   15 dimes   g)   175 pennies

MP-46.   **Algebra Puzzles** Solve each equation. Most answers should be fractions.

a) $3x + 1 = 1$ b) $3x + 1 = 2$

c) $3x + 1 = 3$ d) $5x + 1 = 4$

MP-47.   The flag of Madagascar looks like the picture below right. Use this picture to answer the following questions.

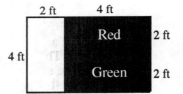

a)   What is the area of the white portion of the flag?

b)   What is the area of the whole flag?

c)   What fraction of the flag is white?

d)   How many rectangles are in Madagascar's flag?   (Hint: The answer is not 3.)

MP-48.   Find the area of each parallelogram.

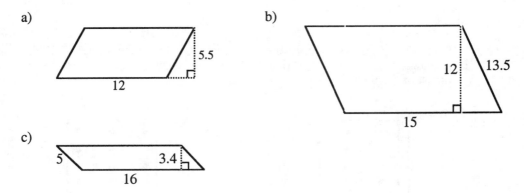

a)

b)

c)

MP-49.   Today your teacher will give you and your partner the vocabulary word flash cards to practice again. The words are from the list in MP-1. Next to the problem number, write the fraction of the cards that you got correct and change this fraction to a percent.

MP-50.   On a dot paper resource page your teacher gives you, draw the rectangle shown at right.

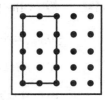

a)   Find the area of the rectangle.

b)   Divide the rectangle as shown in the second figure. Name the two polygons that result. Find the area of each polygon.

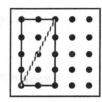

MP-51.   Copy figures (i) and (ii) on a dot paper resource page, then complete parts (a) through (c) that follow.

i)   ii)

a)   For each figure, find the area of the rectangle and the two triangles. Record the areas for each rectangle and triangle on the resource page.

b)   Explain how you know the two triangles are congruent.

c)   How does knowing the triangles are congruent help you know the area of one is half the area of the rectangle?

MP-52.   Copy these figures on a dot paper resource page. Draw the triangle that will complete the rectangle. Use the figure to find the area of the triangles. Be sure to label them with the problem number.

a)   b)

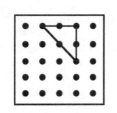

MP-53.   Copy the figure at right on a dot paper resource page.

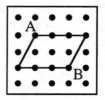

   a)   Find the area of the parallelogram.

   b)   Draw a diagonal from vertex A to vertex B.

   c)   Find the area of each triangle created by the diagonal.

   d)   How is the area of each triangle related to the parallelogram?

MP-54.   Use your conjectures from the previous problems to find the areas below.

   a)   Find the area of each parallelogram.

   b)   Find the area of each triangle.

   i)   ii)

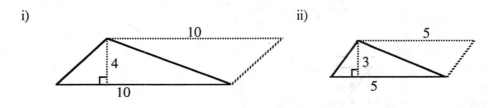

MP-55.

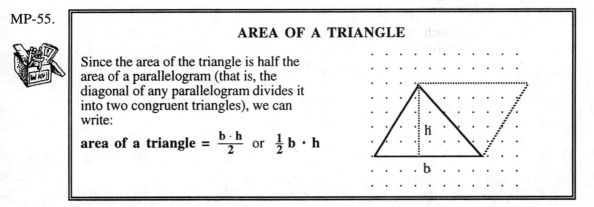

AREA OF A TRIANGLE

Since the area of the triangle is half the
area of a parallelogram (that is, the
diagonal of any parallelogram divides it
into two congruent triangles), we can
write:

area of a triangle = $\dfrac{b \cdot h}{2}$ or $\dfrac{1}{2}b \cdot h$

Make these notes in your Tool Kit to the right of the double-lined box.

   a)   Why do you divide by 2 when finding the area of a triangle?

   b)   Show how to find the area of a triangle with a height of 6 and a base of 7.

MP-56.   Use the ideas from the previous problems to find the areas of the following triangles. Write an equation to show your work. The equation is provided in part (a).

a)
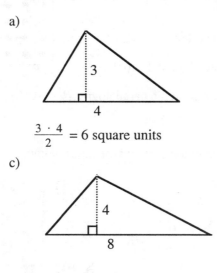

$$\frac{3 \cdot 4}{2} = 6 \text{ square units}$$

b)
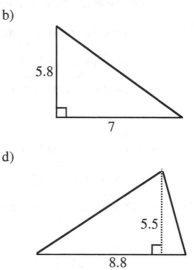

c)
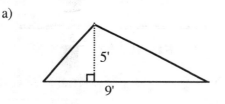

d)

MP-57.   For each triangle, find the area.

a)
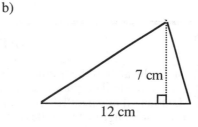

b)

MP-58.

Clarisse made a copy of her state flag for the library.

a)   It was twice as long as it was wide and had an area of 288 square inches. What were its dimensions?

b)   Suppose that Clarisse had made the length of her flag 50% longer than its width so that it had an area of 294 square inches. What would its dimensions have been?

MP-59.   **Algebra Puzzles** Find the number that replaces the variable to make the equation true.

   a) $2x + 1 = 1$ b) $2x + 1 = 2$

   c) $2x + 1 = 3$ d) $2x + 1 = 4$

MP-60.   Draw base ten sketches and label them for the problems below. Show the subproblems
          you use to find the total area.

   a) $15 \cdot 14$ b) $12 \cdot 17$

MP-61.   Mrs. Poppington loves visiting Finland, and really
          likes the geometry of its flag. Finland's flag is
          white with a blue cross.

   a)   Use the diagram of the flag below to find
         the area of the blue cross. Be sure to show
         all of your subproblems.

   b)   What fraction of the flag is represented by
         the area of the blue cross?

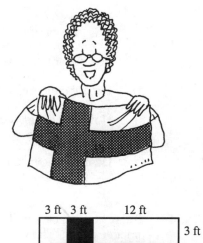

MP-62.   Use your fraction-decimal-percent grid. List the equivalent expressions for the shaded
          area in each box. Be sure you name at least one fraction, one decimal, and one percent.

   a)   b)   c)

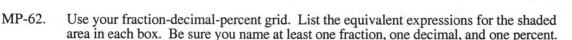

MP-63.   Carol wants to replace the carpet in her hallway that is 6 feet wide. How many square
          feet of carpet will she need for each of the hallway lengths shown in the table below?

   a)   Copy and complete the table below.

Width (feet)	Length (feet)	Area (square feet)
6	4	
6	5	
6	6	
6	8	
6	10	
6	12	
6	15	

   b)   Make a graph of the data above. Put the length on the x-axis and the area on the y-
         axis. Be careful when you choose your intervals.

   c)   Use the graph to determine the length when the area is 54 square feet.

   d)   Describe the steps you took to read the length of the hallway from the graph.

   e)   How else could you determine the width when the length is 6 feet and the area is 54
         square feet?

   f)   Describe the pattern represented by the graph.

MP-64.   Today your teacher will give you and your partner the vocabulary word flash cards to
          practice again. The words are from the list in problem MP-1. Next to the problem
          number, write the fraction of the cards that you got correct and change this fraction to a
          percent.

MP-65.   For each of the following questions, draw the picture that satisfies the conditions
          described. Use grid or graph paper.

   a)   Draw a quadrilateral with an area of 15 square units.

   b)   Draw a parallelogram that is not a rectangle with an area of 15 square units.

   c)   Draw a right triangle with an area of 7.5 square units.

   d)   Draw an acute triangle with an area of 7.5 square units.

   e)   Draw a rectangle with an area of 6 square units and a perimeter of 10.

MP-66. We can use what we know about finding the area of rectangles to find the areas of more complicated figures. Working with the other members of your team, find the areas of each of the shapes below. In parts (b) and (c), you may need to find some missing measurements. When you have to solve a smaller problem before you can solve a larger problem, you have broken the problem into **subproblems**. For example, in part (a) you need to compute the areas of two rectangles (two subproblems) and add the results (a third subproblem) to get the total area.

a)   b)   c)

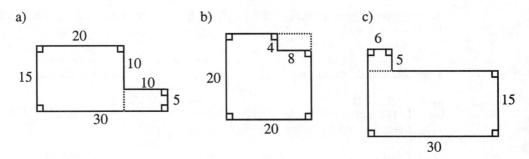

MP-67. Look again at the figures in parts (b) and (c) of the previous problem.

a) Carlos said he could compute the area of the figure by taking the area of the big square (20 · 20 = 400) and subtracting the area of the little rectangle. Is Carlos right? Explain in one or two complete sentences.

b) With other members of your team, look at part (c) in the previous problem and show two different ways to break up the area into rectangles.

MP-68. Find the area of the figure at right both by adding the areas of two rectangles and also by subtracting the area of a smaller rectangle from the larger one's area. What subproblem(s) do you need to complete before you can calculate the area of the smaller rectangle?

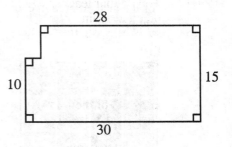

MP-69. Copy each figure onto your paper, write in any needed dimensions that are missing, and compute both the area and the perimeter.

a)   b)

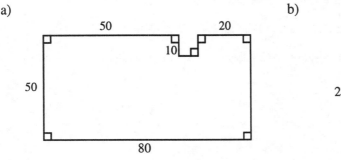

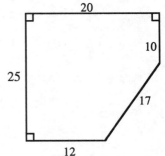

Mrs. Poppington Sees the World: Area and Multiplication   121

MP-70. An equilateral triangle of side length L has a height of approximately 0.866L.
        For example, if L = 10 cm, then its height is approximately 8.66 cm.

   a)   Sketch an equilateral triangle on your paper.

   b)   Find the approximate heights of three equilateral triangles of side lengths 10
        centimeters, 20 inches, and 8 feet.

   c)   An equilateral triangle has a height of 6 cm. About how long is each side?

MP-71. Simplify each expression.

   a) $|-24| - |45|$ b) $|41| - |-22|$

   c) $-|48|$ d) $-|-7|$

MP-72. **Algebra Puzzles**   Solve these equations.

   a) $2x + 7 = 2$ b) $4x + 3 = 10$

   c) $1 - 4x = 3$ d) $4 = 4x + 1$

MP-73. Use your fraction-decimal-percent grid. Write a sentence that lists equivalent expressions
        for the shaded area in each box. Be sure to name at least one fraction, one decimal, and
        one percent.

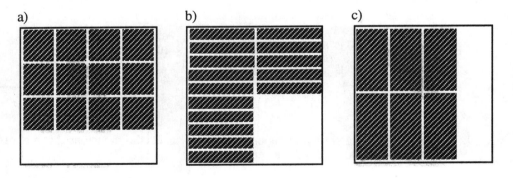

MP-74.   When Mrs. Poppington first arrived in Kuwait, the temperature equaled the average annual high temperature of the country. The next day, the temperature was the same, and the day after that, the temperature was one degree lower. The sum of those three numbers was 377. Use a Guess and Check table to help you find the temperature on that first day.

MP-75.   A regular hexagon can be divided into six equilateral triangles.

a)   Sketch a regular hexagon and show how this can happen.

b)   Find the area of a regular hexagon with a side length of 10 inches.

MP-76.   Today your teacher will give you and your partner the vocabulary word flash cards to practice again. The words are from the list in MP-1. Next to the problem number, write the fraction of the cards that you got correct and change this fraction to a percent.

MP-77.   **Area Problems** Your teacher will show you each of the six shapes below. You and your partner will discuss the area of each shape and write down its area.

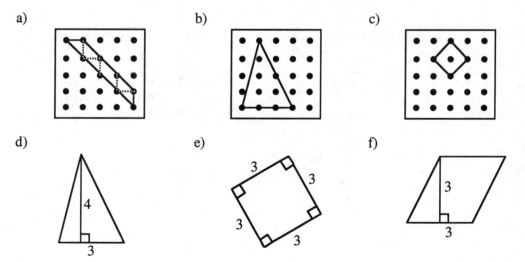

a)

b)

c)

d)

e)

f)

MP-78.   Use an index card or the square corner of a piece of paper to find the line perpendicular to each of the lines at the indicated points on the resource page.

Example: a)

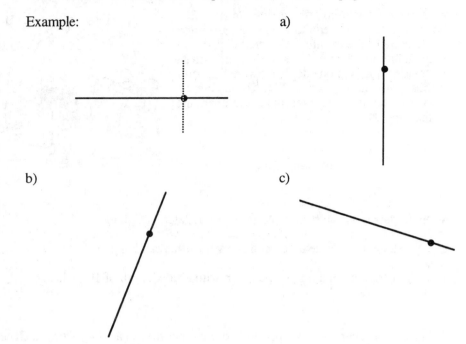

b)   c)

MP-79.   Any side of a triangle (or rectangle or parallelogram) can be used as a base, but usually it is easiest to use the horizontal side if you can. Then the height (sometimes called the altitude) is vertical, since it is perpendicular to the base. Sometimes the base of a triangle needs to be extended so that it meets the height.

a)   For the triangle below, what are the lengths of the base (b) and height (h)?

b)   Verify that the area of this triangle can be found using $\frac{1}{2}$ b · h.

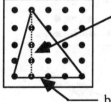

height (Think of the height as the "distance a bowling ball falls when dropped from the top vertex.")

base (side that "sits flat on the ground")

MP-80.   Use the triangle at right for this problem.

a)   What are the lengths of b and h?

b)   Verify that the area of this triangle can be found using $\frac{1}{2}$ b · h. Will subproblems help you?

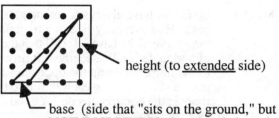

height (to <u>extended</u> side)

base (side that "sits on the ground," but NOT INCLUDING the extended portion)

MP-81.   Find the areas of the following triangles. Show your work.

a)   b)   c)   d)

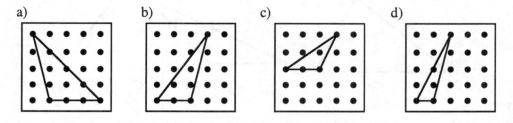

MP-82.   For each of the triangles below:

a)   Copy them onto dot paper.

b)   Mark one side as the base and draw a height from the opposite vertex to that base (or extended side).

c)   Use the formula to find the area of each triangle. You may want to reorient the triangles (that is, turn the page to view them in a different way).

i)   ii)

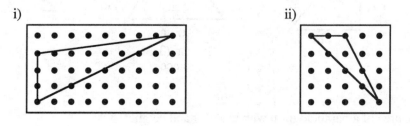

MP-83.   So far we have always found heights down to a horizontal   Example:
          base. However, any side of a triangle or parallelogram
          may serve as its base. Recall that the definition of a height
          of a triangle is a line segment from a vertex perpendicular
          to the line containing the opposite side. Use the resource
          page and try rotating each figure so that each side, one at a
          time, is the horizontal side. A good sticky note works well
          as a straightedge for drawing
          heights, because you can align its edges for the right angle
          and put the sticky side down along the height you want to
          draw.

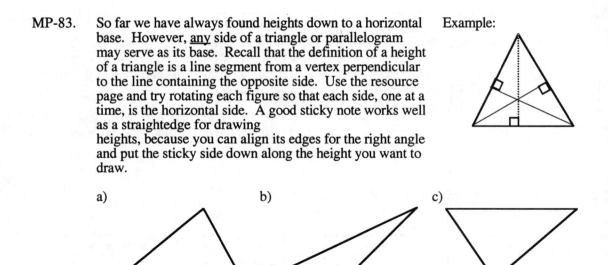

a)   b)   c)

MP-84.   Use a base ten sketch to calculate 12 · 16. Show the subproblems you use to find the
          total area.

MP-85.   Find the areas of the triangles below. Write equations that show how you found the areas.

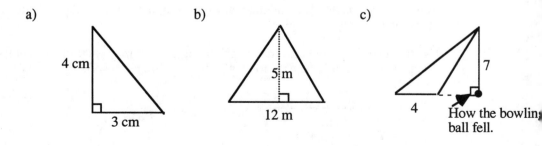

a)   b)   c)

4 cm

3 cm

5 m

12 m

7

4

How the bowling
ball fell.

MP-86.   The area of a parallelogram with base 1.4 and height 0.5 is:

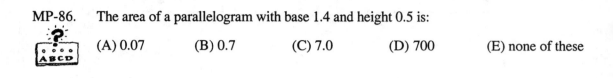

          (A) 0.07   (B) 0.7   (C) 7.0   (D) 700   (E) none of these

MP-87.   When Mrs. Poppington visited Australia, she
was amazed at the number of people on a
football team. When she asked her host how
many players were on each side, he gave this
answer: "Take the number of players, multiply it
by 6 and add 7. That answer is 115." Use a
Guess and Check table to help Mrs. Poppington
figure out how many players are on a team, or
write an equation and work backward.

MP-88.   Jonathan claims that $7 + 3 \cdot 9 = 90$. Explain why he is NOT correct. Then show him
how to modify the expression on the left side so that the result is 90.

MP-89.   Use a base ten sketch to calculate $21 \cdot 6$. Show the subproblems you use to find the total
area.

MP-90.   Recall that a trapezoid has (exactly) one pair of parallel sides. Use subproblems, not the
area formula, to do parts (a) through (d) below.

a)   Compute the area of trapezoid (i) at   i)
right.

b)   What subproblems did you solve in
part (a)?

c)   Compute the area of trapezoid (ii) at
right.

ii)

d)   What subproblems did you need to
solve for part (c)?

MP-91.   Show the calculations you use to find the area of each of these triangles.

a)   b)

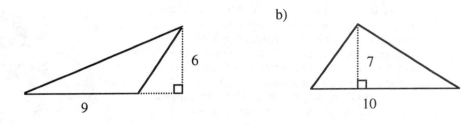

MP-92.   Follow your teacher's instruction for practicing mental math. Show the method you think
          is best.

MP-93.   Mrs. Green's class has been given a plot of land for
          a garden. Before the students start planting, they
          want to apply fertilizer. An expert at the garden
          store tells them that the fertilizer they should use
          comes in bags that cover 100 square feet.

          a)   What do they need to do first to find out how
                much fertilizer is needed?

          b)   What would they do next to calculate the
                amount of fertilizer to buy?

MP-94.   Clark measured the garden. It
          is a rectangle 59 feet long and
          46 feet wide.

          It is possible to build and
          sketch the garden's area using
          the base ten block model.

          This would be a lot of work,
          however. There is a faster
          way. Look at the drawing of
          the model at right. It has four
          regions: one filled with
          hundreds, two filled with
          tens, and another filled with
          ones. The blocks of the
          regions in this picture are
          either 1 x 1 blocks, 1 x 10 blocks, or 10 x 10 blocks. Because there are so many
          blocks involved, most people avoid drawing all the blocks by sketching a rectangle
          with four regions, as shown below.

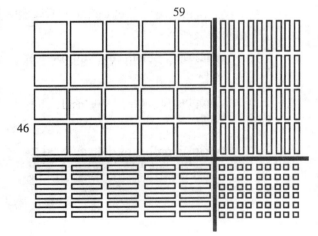

>>**Problem continues on the next page.>>**

a) Start by drawing a large rectangle cut into four regions. Separate the base number into two parts and label the dimensions: one for the tens place (50) and one for the ones place (9). Then make the same separations for the height (40 and 6). We call this type of picture of a multiplication problem a **generic rectangle** model. It is "generic" because it does not show specific numbers of blocks.

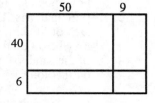

b) Find the areas of the four rectangles. The first one is done for you.

c) Find the total area of the garden.

d) How many bags of fertilizer does Mrs. Green's class need to buy? Explain how you know.

MP-95. The grass on the playing field needs to be reseeded. Again, we need to know the area of the field in order to decide how much seed to buy. The field is 325 feet by 165 feet. We can use a generic rectangle to break this problem into subproblems that are easier to multiply.

a) On your paper, sketch a copy of the generic rectangle for the playing field shown above.

b) Explain how Mrs. Green's students will find the areas for each part of the generic rectangle.

c) Write the subproblems inside each part of the generic rectangle.

d) What is the total area of the playing field? Explain how you got your answer.

e) If a bag of grass seed covers 2500 square feet, how many bags will be needed to plant the playing field's grass?

MP-96.   Since Mrs. Green's class successfully determined
how much fertilizer to buy for the garden, the school
principal, Ms. Torres, has asked them to find the
area of the kindergarten's sandbox so that a tarp
may be ordered to cover it when it rains. The bottom
of the sandbox area is a rectangle 32 feet wide and
64 feet long.

a)   Sketch and label a generic rectangle model for
32 · 64.

b)   Use the generic rectangle you just sketched to
find the area covered by the sandbox.

MP-97.   Read the information in the following box, then sketch and use a generic rectangle to find
the areas for parts (a) and (b) below.

GENERIC RECTANGLES FOR MULTIPLICATION

A **GENERIC RECTANGLE** is a useful
way to organize a multiplication problem.

Step 1: Sketch a rectangle.

Step 2: Label the dimensions with numbers
that represent each of the place values
in the problem.

Step 3: Fill in the interior rectangular regions
with the <u>partial</u> <u>products</u> like a
multiplication table.

Step 4: Add the partial products to get the
total area.

Example: 347 · 28

	300 +	40	+ 7
20 +	6000	800	140
8	2400	320	56

347 · 28

```
     6000
     2400
      800
      320
      140
 +     56
    9716
```

a)   95 · 39   b)   124 · 34

MP-98. Juliana was compiling the results for the volleyball season and listed the total number of games won by each of the 20 teams in the league. The number of games won by the different teams during the season were 42, 13, 22, 45, 37, 55, 24, 22, 38, 29, 31, 49, 19, 22, 40, 51, 35, 28, 33, and 38.

a) Make a stem-and-leaf plot showing the number of games won by each team.

b) Find the mean number of games won.

c) Find the median number of games won.

d) Find the mode number of games won.

MP-99. **Algebra Puzzles** Solve each equation. Do **NOT** use a calculator. You will see that you do not need one.

a) $894x - 937 = -937$

b) $426 + 427x = -1$

c) $6432x + 6432 = 0$

d) $-94378x = 0$

MP-100. Recently Mrs. Poppington had a chance to visit the Czech Republic. She was surprised to find that the Czech Republic's flag has the same colors as the American flag (red on the bottom, white on the top, and blue on the left). Use the flag at right to find the area of each different section of the Czech flag. Be sure to show all of your subproblems.

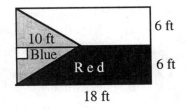

MP-101. Use subproblems to find the area of each of these figures.

a) trapezoid

b) the shaded area between the two rectangles

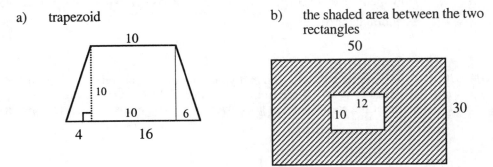

>>**Problem continues on the next page.**>>

c)

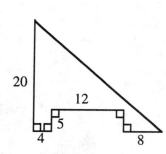

MP-102.   Sketch a rectangle (or rectangles) to illustrate each number.

a) $\frac{4}{8}$

b) $\frac{3}{6}$

c) $\frac{5}{2}$

d) $1\frac{1}{6}$

e) $\frac{7}{6}$

f) $2\frac{1}{2}$

g)   Are any of your sketches related to each other? Which ones are, and how are they related?

MP-103.   Answer the questions below. There are two tasks in each part.

a)   How many one-fourths are in $4\frac{1}{4}$? Use your answer to rewrite $4\frac{1}{4}$ as a fraction with a denominator of 4.

b)   How many one-thirds are in $3\frac{2}{3}$? Use your answer to rewrite $3\frac{2}{3}$ as a fraction with a denominator of 3.

c)   How many one-eighths are in $5\frac{5}{8}$? Use your answer to rewrite $5\frac{5}{8}$ as a fraction with a denominator of 8.

d)   How many one-fifths are in $6\frac{4}{5}$? Use your answer to rewrite $6\frac{4}{5}$ as a fraction with a denominator of 5.

MP-104.   Today your teacher will give you and your partner the vocabulary word flash cards to practice again. The words are from the list in MP-1. Next to the problem number, write the fraction of the cards that you got correct and change this fraction to a percent.

MP-105. **Area Problems** Your teacher will show you the six shapes below one at a time. You and your partner will discuss and write down the area of each shape.

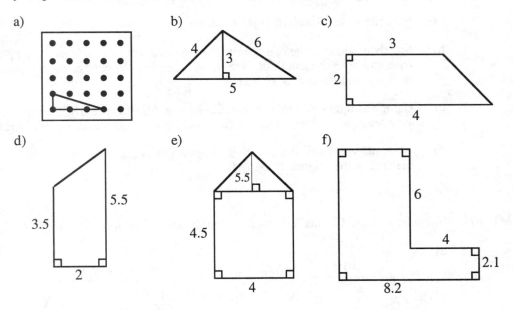

a)

b)

c)

d)

e)

f)

MP-106. A previous problem gave you one way to find the area of a trapezoid by breaking it up into a rectangle and two triangles. There is another way to find the area of a trapezoid, and it leads to a formula like the ones we have for parallelograms, rectangles, and triangles.

a) The resource page your teacher will give you has two pairs of congruent trapezoids. Choose one pair of the trapezoids and carefully cut them out.

b) Measure the **bases** (the parallel sides) and the height of the trapezoid you cut out and record these measurements on your cut-out piece. Use centimeters.

c) Rotate the second copy of the trapezoid so that it is upside down and place it "end to end" with the first. If you do this correctly, this figure will form a parallelogram.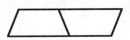

d) What is the base and height of this parallelogram?

e) Find the area of the parallelogram.

f) Using the area that you just found for the parallelogram, find the area of the trapezoid. What is your last step?

MP-107. Christa saw that she could find the area of a trapezoid without cutting. She said that the base of the big parallelogram would be the sum of the two bases of the trapezoid.

   a) Was she right? Explain to your partner.

   b) She then said that she could write the area as a formula. If t is the length of the top base and b is the length of the bottom base, then the base of the big parallelogram is b + t and its area is (b + t) · h.

   c) Using the figure you used in the previous problem, explain to the other members of your team why Christa was correct about how to find the area of the parallelogram.

   d) Now that you know the area of the big parallelogram, what do you need to do to find the area of the original trapezoid?

MP-108. Show how to use Christa's method to find the area of each of these trapezoids.

a)

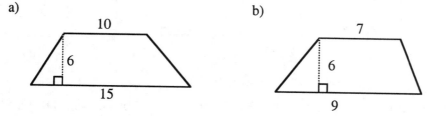

b)

MP-109.

AREA OF A TRAPEZOID

Since the area of the trapezoid is half the area of a parallelogram made with two congruent copies of the trapezoid, we have:

area of a trapezoid = $\frac{1}{2}$ · (b + t) · h or $\frac{b+t}{2}$ · h

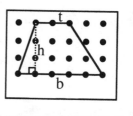

Make these notes in your Tool Kit to the right of the double-lined box.

Show how to use the formula to find the area of a trapezoid with a top base of 6, a lower base of 14, and a height of 8. Check with your partner or team to be sure your example is done correctly.

MP-110. **Lizzie's Awesome Waffles** This recipe serves four.

$1\frac{3}{4}$ cups flour

$1\frac{3}{4}$ cups milk

1 tablespoon baking powder

$\frac{1}{2}$ cup oil

2 eggs

Rewrite the recipe to serve the following numbers
of people. Write fractions greater than one as
mixed numbers.

a)   twelve people   b)   two people

MP-111. Find the area of each figure. Write equations that show your thinking.

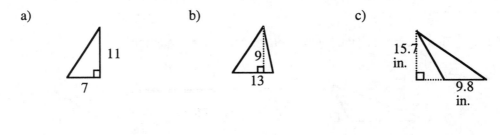

a)   b)   c)

    11   9   15.7
                                                           in.
  7   13   9.8
                                                              in.

MP-112. The value of x that satisfies the equation $2x + 3 = 15$ is:

(A) 9   (B) 6   (C) 7.5   (D) 4.5

MP-113. Sketch and label a generic rectangle for each product. Show the subproblems (partial
products) you use to find the total area.

a) $23 \cdot 12$ b) $25 \cdot 11$

MP-114. Write a letter to a younger student who is learning about two-digit multiplication. Explain
how to multiply $21 \cdot 14$. Use base ten blocks and subproblems (partial products) as part
of your explanation. You may also use other methods to help the student understand the
problem.

MP-115. Mrs. Poppington likes Thai food, so she was very happy to visit Thailand. She saw that the flag of Thailand is broken into five parts. The center stripe is blue, and the top and bottom stripes are red. The other two stripes are white. The red and white stripes are the same size.

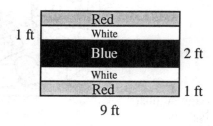

a) Find the total area of both red parts of the flag.

b) Find the area of the blue part of the flag.

c) Find the area of the whole flag.

d) What fraction of the flag is blue?

MP-116. Find the areas of the figures below. Show your equations.

a)

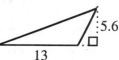

b)

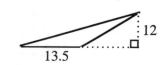

MP-117. The area of a trapezoid with top base 6.3 cm, bottom base 11.7 cm, and height 10 cm is:

(A) 60 cm^2　　　(B) 120 cm^2　　　(C) 90 cm^2　　　(D) 45 cm^2

MP-118. MNEEZ is a Martian whose children each have five legs. One day the power was out and, in total darkness, she had to take their socks out of a drawer that contained 50 red socks and 50 blue socks.

a) How many socks would she have to pull out to be sure one of her children had the same color socks on all five feet?

b) How many socks would she have to pull out to be sure two of her children had the same color socks on all five feet?

c) What would be the answers to parts (a) and (b) if there were also 50 green socks in the drawer?

MP-119. Mrs. Poppington has invited visitors from some of the countries she has visited to come and speak to her class. To make the visitors feel welcome, your team has been asked to create a quilt containing the flag for each visitor's country.

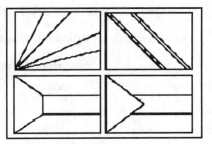

Seychelles:

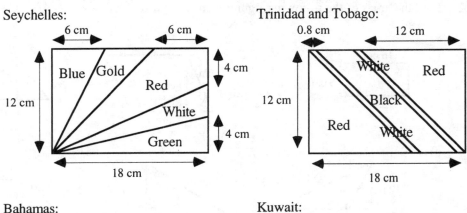

Trinidad and Tobago:

Bahamas:

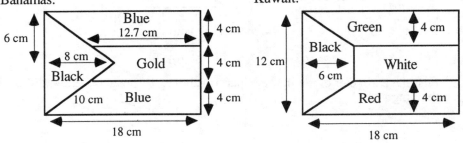

Kuwait:

a) For each flag, make a list of the shapes you see (equilateral triangle, trapezoid, etc.).

b) Determine the area of each shape. Show all of your subproblems.

c) Determine the total area of all the flags combined. That is, determine how much blue, black, gold, red, white, and green material will be needed.

d) Determine the total area of the border you will need to connect the flags. It should be 2 centimeters wide and surround each flag. It will be gold.

e) Place your order for the number of square centimeters of each color material with your teacher, showing all calculations.

MP-120. **Algebra Puzzles** Decide which number belongs in place of the variable to make the equation true.

a) $13 - 5x = 7$

b) $6x - 8 = 0$

c) $4x - 1 = -3$

d) $4x - 1 = -4$

MP-121. For each of the following questions, draw the picture on grid or graph paper.

    a)   Draw a quadrilateral with an area of 7 square units and no right angles.

    b)   Draw an obtuse triangle with an area of 3.5 square units.

    c)   Draw a rectangle with an area of 5 square units and a perimeter of 21 units.

MP-122. Find the areas of the following figures. Show your method.

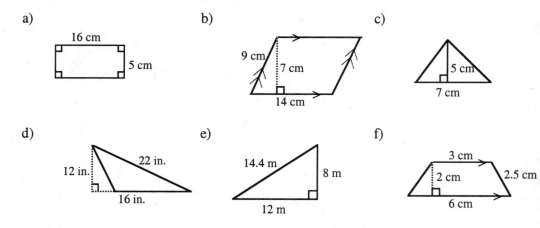

a)

16 cm

5 cm

b)

9 cm

7 cm

14 cm

c)

5 cm

7 cm

d)

12 in.

22 in.

16 in.

e)

14.4 m

8 m

12 m

f)

3 cm

2 cm

2.5 cm

6 cm

MP-123. Find the perimeter of the figure in part (a) above. Write an equation to show your thinking.

MP-124. Complete a Guess and Check table to solve the following problem.

On her tour of the world, Mrs. Poppington stopped in Chicago. The tallest building in Chicago is the Sears Tower. A clever tour guide posed this problem: 417 is 23 less than 4 times the number of stories in the Sears Tower. How many stories does the Tower have?

MP-125. Follow the directions below.
For example, $1\frac{1}{5}$ could be written $6(\frac{1}{5})$ or $\frac{6}{5}$ or even $\frac{1}{5} + \frac{1}{5} + \frac{1}{5} + \frac{1}{5} + \frac{1}{5} + \frac{1}{5}$.

    a)   Write three equivalent expressions for $1\frac{3}{5}$.   b)   Write $\frac{5}{4}$ in three different ways.

    c)   Write $4\frac{2}{3}$ as a fraction.   d)   Write $\frac{15}{4}$ as a mixed number.

MP-126.   Follow your teacher's instructions for practicing mental math.

MP-127.

Chapter Summary   Your teacher will give you the flash cards you used earlier in the chapter. With your partner, decide who should be quizzed first. Be sure your partner keeps track of the ones you get and the ones you miss by making two stacks or by making a list of the ones you miss.

a)   On your paper, write this list and put a check by the ones you should study further.

b)   What was your percent correct this time? How much have you improved since the first time?

MP-128.   Find the area of the shaded portion of each rectangle.

a)   b)

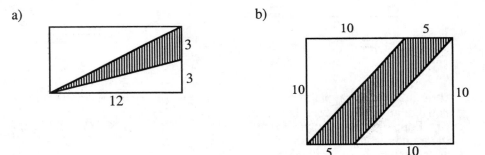

MP-129.   Use a generic rectangle to multiply $25 \cdot 18$.

MP-130. Show the calculation for each subproblem you use to find the area for each of these figures.

a)   trapezoid

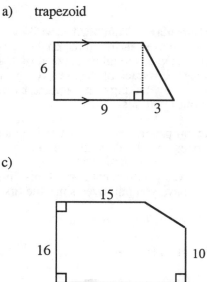

b)   trapezoid

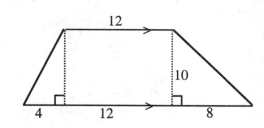

c)

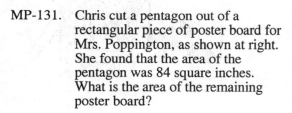

MP-131. Chris cut a pentagon out of a rectangular piece of poster board for Mrs. Poppington, as shown at right. She found that the area of the pentagon was 84 square inches. What is the area of the remaining poster board?

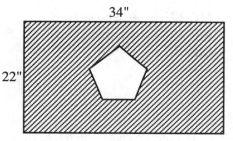

MP-132. Find the area of the shaded portion of each rectangle.

a)

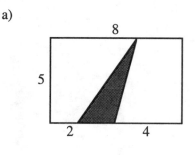

b)   The shaded region is a parallelogram.

MP-133. Use subproblems to find the area of each figure.

a)

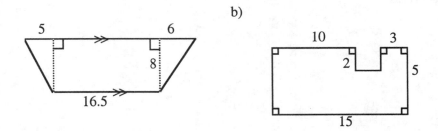

b)

MP-134. Sketch and use a generic rectangle to find the following products.

a)   23 · 52

b)   132 · 26

MP-135. **What We Have Done in This Chapter**

Below is a list of the Tool Kit entries from this chapter.

- MP-1   Geometric Vocabulary
- MP-16   Area of a Rectangle
- MP-20   Congruence
- MP-26   Base and Height of a Parallelogram
- MP-43   Area of a Parallelogram
- MP-55   Area of a Triangle
- MP-109   Area of a Trapezoid

Review all the entries and read the notes you made in your Tool Kit. Make a list of any questions, terms, or notes you do not understand. Ask your partner or study team members for help. If anything is still unclear, ask your teacher.

THE GIANT ONE

Chapter 5

Chapter 5
The Giant 1: RATIOS, MEASUREMENT, AND EQUIVALENT FRACTIONS

You will begin this chapter by using tables to show the relationship between pairs of numbers called ratios. The ratio tables will help you solve word problems involving unit costs, rates, and proportions. Throughout the chapter you will practice several methods for finding equivalent fractions. The Fraction Blackout game will help you recognize equivalent fractions. In the Diamond Problems, you practice working with integers. You will practice your measurement skills in several activities.

In this chapter you will have the opportunity to:

- solve problems that include ratios, unit costs, rates, and proportions by using ratio tables.

- find equivalent fractions using fraction bars, rulers, the Identity Property of Multiplication, and a model.

- practice integer operations.

- develop an understanding of inequality.

- measure and identify lengths with a ruler.

Read the problem below, but **do not try to solve it now**. What you learn over the next few days will enable you to solve it.

GO-0.   **One for the Giant**

Patricia Garcia was reading a story to her sister, Ana, about a kindly giant who lived in a very cold place. Ana felt sorry for the giant and wanted to make him a quilt just like hers (only bigger, of course). Ana's quilt is 3744 square inches and took 104 hours to make. Ana wants the giant quilt to be 9360 square inches. If she makes the giant quilt at the same rate at which she made her quilt, how long will it take to make?

Number Sense		
Algebra and Functions		
Mathematical Reasoning		
Measurement and Geometry		
Statistics, Data Analysis, & Probability		

Chapter 5
The Giant 1: RATIOS, MEASUREMENT, AND EQUIVALENT FRACTIONS

GO-1.

> ## RATIOS
>
> A **RATIO** is a comparison of two quantities by division. It can be written in several ways, such as: $\dfrac{2}{5}$ 2 : 5   2 to 5

Make these notes in your Tool Kit to the right of the double-lined box.

a)   Write the ratio "three to seven" in the three different forms.

b)   Is the order of the numbers in the ratio important? Explain your answer.

GO-2.   Equivalent ratios can be organized in a ratio table. Complete the following ratio tables to record the cost of different weights of fruit. Be prepared to explain your reasoning, that is, how you determined each ratio.

a)
Pounds of Melon	1	2	3	5	6	8
Cost			$2.70	$4.50		

b)
Pounds of Bananas	1	2	3	6	8	9
Cost			$1.02	$2.04		

c)
Pounds of Kiwi	1	2	3	4	8	9
Cost		$5.60				

GO-3.   Use the tables from the previous problem to draw three graphs, one for each data set, on the same coordinate axes. Label the horizontal axis from 1 through 8 and the vertical axis in one-dollar increments.

a)   If you bought zero pounds of fruit, how much would you spend? Label this point on your graph.

b)   What similarities or differences do you see between the graphs?

c)   Which graph is the steepest? Which graph is the flattest?

Examine the table for the cost of candy. Compare it to the data you have graphed, but do not graph the data.

Pounds of Candy	1	2	3	4	5	8
Cost	$2.00	$4.00	$6.00	$8.00	$10.00	$16.00

d)   Answer these questions without graphing the data. If you were to graph the candy data, which graph(s) would it be steeper than?

e)   Which graph(s) would the candy data be flatter than?

GO-4.   Artists use ratios to help them make drawings look like real life. The human face is full of ratios. Use the picture at right to draw a realistic face. You may either draw the face of someone you know or draw a copy of the face provided here. Some guidelines are:

a)   The face should be 6 units high and 4 units wide.

b)   The eyes are half-way between the top and bottom of the face.

c)   Each eye is one unit wide and the space between them is one unit.

d)   The mouth is one unit wide.

e)   Finish your drawing using the drawing at right to help you.

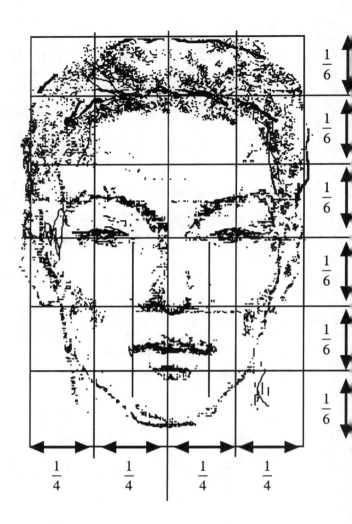

GO-5.   Steve drives 65 miles per hour. Copy and complete the ratio table below.

Miles	65					
Hours	1	2				

a)   How many hours does it take for Steve to travel from Providence to New York, a distance of 130 miles?

b)   How far can he travel in four hours?

c)   How long will it take him to travel 390 miles?

d)   How far can he travel in eight hours?

GO-6.   In a class of 20 students, there were nine boys. Copy and use a ratio table like the one below to determine how many boys there would be in a class of 100 students.

Number of Boys	9				
Total Students	20	40			

a)   Based on the data in your table, about what percent of the class is boys?

b)   What percent of the class is girls?

GO-7.

MIXED NUMBERS AND FRACTIONS GREATER THAN ONE

The number $4\frac{1}{4}$ is called a **MIXED NUMBER**, because it is made from a whole number, 4, and a fraction, $\frac{1}{4}$. It is a mix of a whole number and a fraction.

The number $\frac{17}{4}$ is a fraction that is greater than one, because the numerator is greater than the denominator. Sometimes fractions that are greater than one are called "improper fractions." "Improper" does not mean "wrong." In mathematics, keeping a fraction in its "improper form" is often more useful than changing it to a mixed number.

Make these notes in your Tool Kit.

a)   Highlight the words "a whole number and a fraction" and "fraction that is greater than one."

b)   Write the label "Mixed Numbers" and give three examples in the space to the right of the double-lined box.

c)   Write three examples of fractions greater than one to the right of the double-lined box.

GO-8.   **Algebra Puzzles** Write three pairs of numbers that make each of the following equations true. Write your answers as ordered pairs (x, y). For example, (1, 3) is an answer for part (a). Remember you can use negative numbers as well.

a) $x + y = 4$ b) $x + y = 10$

c) $x + y = 0$ d) $x + y = 1$

GO-9.   In the trapezoid at right, all dimensions are in feet. Find the perimeter and area.

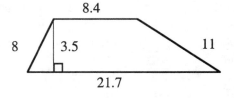

GO-10. George saved $58 in two weeks. At this rate, approximately how long will it take him to save at least $830?

(A) 29 weeks   (B) 12 weeks   (C) 14 weeks   (D) 23 weeks

GO-11. Now that we have started a new chapter, it is time for you to organize your binder.

a) Put the work from the last chapter in order and keep it in a separate folder.

b) When this is completed, write, "I have organized my binder."

GO-12. **Diamond Problems** With your partner, study the examples of Diamond Problems in the table below. See if you can discover a pattern.

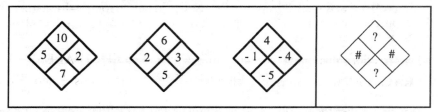

In the fourth diamond, can you find the unknowns (?) if you know the numbers (#)? Exp how you would do this. Note that "#" is a standard symbol for the word "number."

Copy the Diamond Problems below and use the pattern you found to complete each of the

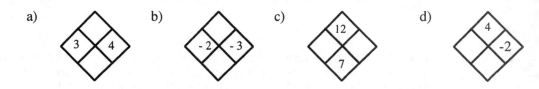

GO-13. Today you will be making a set of fraction bars.

a) Label each fractional part as shown on <u>both</u> of the resource pages.

b) Cut along the darkened (horizontal) lines to create strips. Put your initials on the bac of each piece. Do <u>not</u> cut along vertical lines except for the ends of each strip.

c) Find two pieces the exact same length to make $\frac{1}{2}$. Write an equation in the form of

$\frac{1}{2} =$ ____ to explain what you found.

d)   Find four pieces the exact same length to make $\frac{1}{2}$. Write an equation in the form of $\frac{1}{2} = $ ____ to explain what you found.

e)   Find two pieces the exact same length to make $\frac{1}{4}$. Write an equation in the form of $\frac{1}{4} = $ ____ to explain what you found.

f)   Find four pieces the exact same length to make $\frac{2}{3}$. Write an equation in the form of $\frac{2}{3} = $ ____ to explain what you found.

g)   Find two pieces the exact same length to make $\frac{1}{3}$. Write an equation in the form of $\frac{1}{3} = $ ____ to explain what you found.

h)   Put all of the pieces in an envelope to keep in your binder for later use.

GO-14.

EQUIVALENT FRACTIONS

Two fractions that name the same number are called **EQUIVALENT FRACTIONS**. For example, because $\frac{1}{2} = \frac{3}{6}$, the fractions $\frac{1}{2}$ and $\frac{3}{6}$ are equivalent.

Make these notes in your Tool Kit to the right of the double-lined box.

a)   Explain why $\frac{1}{3}$ and $\frac{4}{12}$ are equivalent fractions.

b)   Name two other equivalent fractions.

GO-15. Complete the following equivalent fraction ratio tables and make a list of equivalent fractions. You may use your uncut fraction bar resource page for visual assistance. For example, for the ratio table below, where 2N is the variable expression or rule relating N and D, $\frac{1}{2} = \frac{2}{4} = \frac{3}{6}$ is a list of equivalent fractions.

numerator (N)	1	2	3	N
denominator (D)	2	4	6	2N

a)

N	1	2	3	4	25	N
D	4					

b)

N	1		3	4	N
D	3	6			

c)

N	2	4		8	60
D	3		9		

GO-16. Look at your uncut fraction bar resource page. Name a fraction that is:

a) greater than $\frac{1}{2}$ and less than 1.

b) greater than $\frac{1}{4}$, less than $\frac{3}{4}$, and not $\frac{1}{2}$.

c) greater than $\frac{1}{4}$ and less than $\frac{5}{8}$.

d) greater than $\frac{3}{8}$ and less than $\frac{4}{8}$.

Example:

$\frac{1}{2}$
?
1 whole

GO-17. Use your cut fraction bars to model the following problems and write each result as one fraction.

a) $\frac{3}{6} + \frac{2}{6}$

b) $\frac{1}{2} + \frac{1}{3}$

c) $\frac{1}{4} + \frac{2}{4}$

d) $\frac{1}{4} + \frac{1}{2}$

e) $\frac{5}{10} + \frac{2}{10}$

f) $\frac{1}{2} + \frac{1}{5}$

g) Consider the pairs (a) and (b), (c) and (d), and (e) and (f). What do you notice about the answers to these pairs?

GO-18. Jeanine earns $5.50 an hour baby-sitting her neighbors' three children. Copy and complete the following ratio table to determine how much she should charge her neighbor.

a) How much will Jeanine earn if she starts at 7:30 p.m. and ends at 12:30 a.m.?

b) How much will she earn if the neighbors do not return for $5\frac{1}{2}$ hours?

Hours	1	2	3	4	5	6	N
Amount							

GO-19. A bank teller can count 150 bills each minute.

a) How many can he count in five minutes? Ten minutes? Thirty minutes? One hour? Create a ratio table to solve this problem.

b) How many bills will he count each day if he counts for 8 hours a day?

c) How many bills can he count in five days, 14 days, and 365 days? You may use another ratio table to solve this problem.

GO-20. Using the numbers 0, 1, 2, $2\frac{1}{2}$, 3, 7, $7\frac{1}{2}$, 9, and 10, answer the following questions. (You may use a number more than once.)

a) Find five numbers with a mean of 5.

b) Find five numbers with a mean of 5 and a median of $2\frac{1}{2}$.

c) If you have a mean of 5, what is the largest median you can have for this set of numbers?

GO-21. Simplify each expression.

a) $4 \cdot (8 - 4) + 3$

b) $(20 - 5) - 4 \cdot 8 + 2$

c) $2 \cdot 3 + 1 + 5 \cdot 4$

d) $6 \cdot 2 + 3 \cdot 8 + 6$

GO-22. Practice mental math according to your teacher's directions. Explain in writing how you solved one of the problems.

GO-23. Use your fraction bars to solve the following problems and write the result as a fraction.

a) $\frac{2}{6} + \frac{2}{6}$

b) $\frac{5}{6} + \frac{4}{6}$

c) $\frac{3}{4} + \frac{3}{4}$

d) $\frac{5}{8} - \frac{3}{8}$

e) $\frac{5}{10} - \frac{2}{10}$

f) $\frac{1}{2} - \frac{1}{4}$

GO-24. You will create a "Giant Inch" (we will call it an inch even though it really is not an inch long) as part of the classroom's giant ruler. Your teacher will give you a piece of paper.

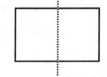

first fold

a) Fold your paper in half as shown. Now unfold your paper and mark the fold line <u>halfway</u> down the paper (from the top) with a **black** marker. Label it $\frac{1}{2}$. Fold your paper back in half.

b) Carefully fold your paper in half once again. Open it up. Mark the new fold lines with a **red** marker one-fourth of the way down the paper. Label them $\frac{1}{4}$ and $\frac{3}{4}$ from left to right. Fold your paper back into fourths.

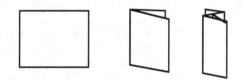

c) Carefully fold your paper in half again. Open it up. Mark these new fold lines with a **green** marker one-eighth of the way down the paper. Label them $\frac{1}{8}$, $\frac{3}{8}$, $\frac{5}{8}$, and $\frac{7}{8}$ from left to right. Fold your paper back into eighths.

d) Fold your paper in half again. Open it up. Mark the new fold lines with a **blue** marker a little way down (about half of one-eighth). Label them $\frac{1}{16}$, $\frac{3}{16}$, $\frac{5}{16}$, $\frac{7}{16}$, $\frac{9}{16}$, $\frac{11}{16}$, $\frac{13}{16}$, and $\frac{15}{16}$ from left to right.

e) When you count by fourths, why do you not mark $\frac{2}{4}$? What fraction is in its place?

f) When you count by eighths, which eighths do you not mark? What other names might each one have?

g) When you count by sixteenths, what numbers do you write with names other than sixteenths? What other names might the "missing" numbers have?

GO-25. Write these line lengths using mixed numbers.

a)

b)

c)

d)

GO-26.

Fraction Blackout
A game for two players.

Mathematical Purpose: To practice finding equivalent fractions.

Object: To fill your game board by strategically choosing which fractions to shade and get your name on the board as a winner.

Materials: One Fraction Blackout game board and one spinner page with spinner. Note: the fraction in each part of the spinner is the value assigned to that sector, NOT the size of the sector. The spinner is not a pie chart.

Scoring: There is no scoring.

How to Play the Game:
- Put your name on your own Fraction Blackout Game Board.
- Decide who will be First Player and who will be Second Player. If three are playing together, decide who will be Third Player.
- First Player chooses and spins either Spinner A or Spinner B.
- First Player records the fraction on the Fraction Blackout Game Board.
- First Player shades the fraction on the Fraction Blackout Game Board. The player may shade any blocks on the Game Board that add to the fraction spun. Both players must agree that the amount filled in is equal to the fraction spun.
- Alternate play.
- If a fraction is spun that is larger than the space the student has left, the student cannot play until the next turn.
- Players may choose which spinner to use (A or B) with each new play.

Ending the Game: Continue to alternate play until one student has filled a Game Board. Other students may continue to play to complete their Game Board.

When you have played Fraction Blackout, raise your hands and give the Fraction Blackout Game Board(s) to your teacher and follow her or his instructions.

GO-27.   Copy and fill in the following equivalent fraction ratio tables, then write a list of equivalent fractions.

a)

N	1			N
D	4	16	8	

b)

N		6	
D	4	8	12

GO-28.   The perimeter of a rectangle is 40 centimeters. It is 1 centimeter longer than it is wide. Use a Guess and Check table to find its width. It will be easier if you draw a picture first.

GO-29.   Use your fraction bars to answer the following questions.

a)   How many one-fourths are in one-half?

b)   How many one-sixths are in two-thirds?

c)   How many one-fourths are in six-eighths?

d)   How many one-halves are in $3\frac{5}{10}$?

GO-30.   Use what you know about rulers to complete the equivalent fractions below.

a) $\frac{2}{16} = \frac{\square}{8}$

b) $\frac{4}{16} = \frac{\square}{8}$

c) $\frac{8}{16} = \frac{1}{\square}$

d) $\frac{10}{16} = \frac{\square}{8}$

e) $\frac{12}{16} = \frac{\square}{4}$

f) $\frac{14}{16} = \frac{\square}{8}$

GO-31.   Farrell is a business man who eats lunch at a different place each day. He keeps track of his lunch expenses. On Monday, he spent $5; on Tuesday, $4.50; on Wednesday, $26.50; on Thursday, $4.75; and on Friday, $4.50.

a)   Calculate the mean of these amounts. Determine the mode and the median.

b)   If you wanted to describe Farrell's spending habits on lunch as fairly as possible, which measure would you use and why?

GO-32.   **Algebra Puzzles**   Write three pairs of numbers that make each equation true.

a) $x - y = 5$

b) $x + y = -5$

c) $x - y = -1$

d) $x - y = -5$

GO-33.   Simplify each expression.

a) $(7 + 6) \cdot 2 \cdot 9 + 6$

b) $(6 + 6) \div 2 - 4 \cdot 4$

c) $5 \cdot (2 + 4) - 7$

d) $6.9 + 2 \cdot 2 \cdot (7 + 8)$

GO-34.   List the fractions below on your paper.

$$\frac{1}{12} \quad \frac{7}{6} \quad \frac{15}{16} \quad \frac{13}{12} \quad \frac{15}{9} \quad \frac{6}{100} \quad \frac{10}{22} \quad \frac{6}{7} \quad \frac{30}{16} \quad \frac{2}{17} \quad \frac{98}{100} \quad \frac{12}{25} \quad \frac{2}{20} \quad \frac{6}{11} \quad \frac{6}{5} \quad \frac{6}{2} \quad \frac{20}{11}$$

a)   List the fractions that are <u>close to</u> or <u>greater than</u> $1\frac{1}{2}$, then cross them off your original list.

b)   List the fractions that are <u>close to</u> 1, then cross them out.

c)   List the fractions that are <u>close to</u> $\frac{1}{2}$, then cross them out.

d)   List the fractions that are <u>close to</u> 0, then cross them out.

GO-35.   For each of the following problems, be sure to write the complete fraction on your paper.

a)   Complete these fractions to make them <u>close to</u> 0: $\frac{\square}{16} , \frac{\square}{10} , \frac{4}{\square} , \frac{10}{\square}$.

b)   Rewrite these fractions to make them <u>close to</u> $\frac{1}{2}$: $\frac{\square}{15} , \frac{\square}{9} , \frac{4}{\square} , \frac{10}{\square}$.

c)   Rewrite these fractions to make them <u>greater than</u> 1 but <u>less than</u> 2:

$$\frac{6}{\square} , \frac{10}{\square} , \frac{\square}{6} , \frac{\square}{3}$$.

GO-36.   Answer each question and write an example for each part below.

a)   If the numerator is very small compared to the size of the denominator, what whole number will the fraction be closest to on a number line?

b)   If the numerator is about half the size of the denominator, where will the fraction be on the number line?

c)   If the numerator of a fraction is about the same size as the denominator, where will the fraction be on a number line?

d)   If the numerator of a fraction is larger than the denominator, where will the fraction be on the number line?

GO-37.   Use equivalent fraction ratio tables or fraction bars to complete parts (a) through (c).

a)   Write two fractions that are the same as $\frac{1}{2}$.

b)   Write two fractions that are the same as $\frac{3}{5}$.

c)   Write two fractions that are the same as $\frac{4}{7}$.

GO-38.   The sum of $\frac{15}{16} + \frac{6}{5} + \frac{6}{7} + \frac{5}{6}$ is approximately:

(A) 1   (B) 2   (C) 3   (D) 4

GO-39.   Anthony and David each bought a personal pizza. Anthony's pizza was cut into five pieces, and he ate three of them. David ate four of his seven pieces. Answer the questions below to help you decide who ate the most pizza. Remember that listing equivalent fractions is just like making a ratio table.

a)   Complete the list below to find the first seven equivalent fractions for $\frac{3}{5}$.

b)   Write the first seven equivalent fractions for $\frac{4}{7}$.

c)   Find a fraction from the first set you wrote that has the same denominator as a fraction from the second set. Write them next to each other.

d)   The fractions $\frac{21}{35}$ and $\frac{20}{35}$ have **common denominators**; that is, their denominators are the same (35). By comparing the numerators, you can see which one is the larger fraction. If the pizzas were cut into 35 pieces, how many pieces would Anthony have eaten? How many would David have eaten?

GO-40.   Which is larger, $\frac{3}{4}$ or $\frac{11}{16}$?

a)   Write lists of equivalent fractions for the two values until you find fractions with common (same) denominators.

b)   Which fraction is larger?

GO-41.

┌───┐
│   **INEQUALITY SYMBOLS**   │
│   │
│ The symbol > means "**is greater than**" and the symbol < means "**is less than.**" │
│ These symbols are called **INEQUALITY SYMBOLS** and are used to compare and │
│ order numbers. For example, $5 > 3$ and $1 < 7$. The symbol ≥ means "is greater than │
│ or equal to" and ≤ means "is less than or equal to."   │
│   │
│ Here is an easy way to remember what each inequality symbol means: the pointed │
│ part of the symbol always points to the smaller number, and the open part of the │
│ symbol always points to the larger number.   │
└───┘

Make these notes in your Tool Kit to the right of the double-lined box.

Rewrite the following expressions placing the correct inequality symbol between them.

a)   3 ___ -2   b)   -5 ___ 2   c)   -3 ___ -7

d)   How will you help yourself to remember which direction the inequality symbol should go?

GO-42.   Jan drove 120 miles in 3 hours.

a)   How far would Jan drive in 12 hours if she kept going at the same rate? Use a ratio table.

b)   How far did Jan drive in half an hour if she always drove at the same rate?

c)   How long would it take Jan to drive 100 miles? Explain your reasoning. Write your answer as a mixed number.

GO-43.   Use your fraction bars to decide which fraction should replace each variable to make the following equations true. Some problems may have more than one answer.

a) $\frac{1}{4} = A + A$ b) $\frac{3}{4} = B + C$ c) $\frac{1}{3} = D + E$

d) $\frac{1}{2} = F + G + G$ e) $\frac{2}{3} = H + I + I$ f) $\frac{7}{8} = J + K$

GO-44. The sum $\frac{7}{16} + \frac{3}{5} + \frac{4}{7} + \frac{3}{7}$ is approximately:

(A) 1   (B) 2   (C) 3   (D) 4

GO-45. The local Little League is having its annual Pancake Breakfast, and Josh and Jean are helping their father make the batter. The recipe makes 50 pancakes and calls for 12 cups of flour.

a) How much flour would Josh need for 200 pancakes? Use a ratio table or show another method.

b) How many pancakes can Josh make with 60 cups of flour?

GO-46. Find the area and perimeter of each of these figures. All dimensions are in feet. Be sure your answers are in proper units.

a)

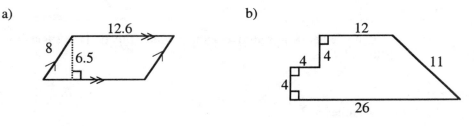

b)

GO-47. Rewrite the following statements using >, <, or = to make each one true. Solve them by thinking, not by calculating and not by using a calculator.

a) $\frac{3}{6}$ —— $\frac{11}{22}$ b) $\frac{2}{2}$ —— $\frac{3}{4}$ c) $\frac{9}{7}$ —— $\frac{3}{3}$

GO-48. These comparisons are more difficult than those in the previous problem. Complete the steps below for each pair of fractions to write a correct inequality.

a) Make a list of equivalent fractions to compare each pair.

b) Clearly show the comparisons using a common denominator for each pair. Look at problem GO-39 if you need help.

i) $\frac{3}{4}$ —— $\frac{5}{6}$ ii) $\frac{4}{9}$ —— $\frac{1}{3}$ iii) $\frac{3}{8}$ —— $\frac{1}{3}$

GO-49. **Diamond Problems** Copy the Diamond Problems below and use the pattern you discovered (shown in the icon under the problem number) to complete each.

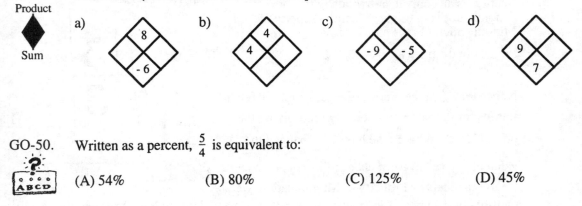

Product

Sum

a)

b)

c)

d)

GO-50. Written as a percent, $\frac{5}{4}$ is equivalent to:

(A) 54%   (B) 80%   (C) 125%   (D) 45%

GO-51. Answer the following questions regarding multiplication.

a)   What is $453 \cdot 1$? $\frac{1}{3} \cdot 1$? $N \cdot 1$?

b)   Describe what happens to a number when you multiply it by 1.

GO-52.

IDENTITY PROPERTY OF MULTIPLICATION

Any number multiplied by 1 equals itself; that is, it remains unchanged. This is called the **IDENTITY PROPERTY OF MULTIPLICATION**.

$$7 \cdot 1 = 7 \qquad -3 \cdot 1 = -3 \qquad x \cdot 1 = x$$

Include these examples of the Identity Property of Multiplication in your Tool Kit to the right of the double-lined box.

Complete each equation.

a) $-4 \cdot 1 =$ ___   b) $4 \cdot 1 =$ ___   c) $B \cdot$ ___ $= B$

GO-53. Complete the ratio table below to find equivalent fractions for $\frac{2}{3}$. We will refer to this table later.

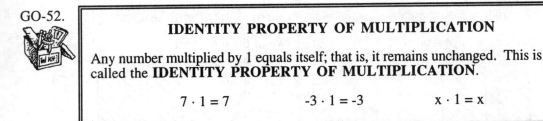

Numerator	2	4	6		12
Denominator	3			12	

GO-54. Write three equivalent fractions for the number 1.

GO-55.   We have previously found equivalent fractions using a ratio table. A quicker method to rename a fraction as an equivalent fraction with a new denominator is to use the Identity Property of Multiplication. In the case at right, the 1 is in disguise as $\frac{3}{3}$.

Notice that $\frac{6}{9}$ and the original $\frac{2}{3}$ are **just different names** for the same number. By multiplying the original fraction by $\frac{3}{3}$, we have not changed the value of $\frac{2}{3}$; we have just changed its name. When we use the Identity Property of Multiplication, we multiply by 1 in one of its fractional forms. We can call it the Giant **1** to remind ourselves of what it really represents, the Identity Property of Multiplication.

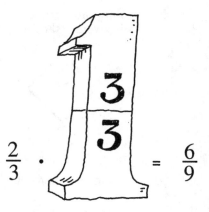

$$\frac{2}{3} \cdot \qquad = \frac{6}{9}$$

Practice using the Giant **1** by doing the problems below. Write the fraction you use for the Giant **1** <u>each</u> <u>time</u> in each part.

a) $\frac{2}{3} \cdot \boxed{1} = \overline{12}$ 　　　 b) $\frac{2}{3} \cdot \boxed{1} = \overline{15}$ 　　　 c) $\frac{2}{3} \cdot \boxed{1} = \overline{18}$

GO-56.   Another way to show the effect of multiplying by $\frac{3}{3}$ is to start with a rectangle in which we have represented $\frac{2}{3}$ by shading two of the three parts.

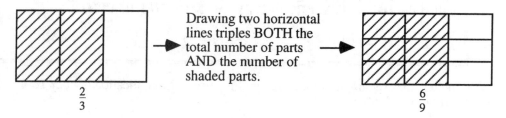

Drawing two horizontal lines triples BOTH the total number of parts AND the number of shaded parts.

$$\frac{2}{3} \qquad\qquad \frac{6}{9}$$

The second rectangle shows the effect of multiplying <u>both</u> the numerator and the denominator of $\frac{2}{3}$ by three, and the equation below represents the relationship shown by the rectangles.

$$\frac{2}{3} \cdot \frac{3}{3} = \frac{6}{9}$$

a)   Draw a rectangle like the first one and label it $\frac{2}{3}$.

b)   Draw another rectangle like the one you drew in part (a). Then draw horizontal lines to represent multiplying by $\frac{4}{4}$.

c)   Write an equation that represents the relationship between the two rectangles you drew.

GO-57.   Consider the three methods you just used to show equivalent fractions: ratio tables, the Giant **1**, and the rectangular area model. How are they similar? How are they different?

GO-58.   Use vertical lines in a rectangle to create and shade $\frac{3}{4}$. Use a horizontal line to double the number of spaces. Write an equation using the Identity Property of Multiplication (Giant **1**) to summarize what you did.

GO-59.   Copy the following problems onto your paper and show how to multiply by 1 to create equivalent fractions. Replace the $\mathbb{1}$ with a fraction and complete the equivalent fraction.

a) $\frac{1}{3} \cdot \mathbb{1} = \frac{}{24}$ b) $\frac{}{12} = \frac{3}{4} \cdot \mathbb{1}$ c) $\frac{2}{5} \cdot \mathbb{1} = \frac{12}{}$

d)   Copy part (a) in your Tool Kit to the right of the double-lined box for the Identity Property of Multiplication.

GO-60.   Suppose we want to compare $\frac{3}{5}$ and $\frac{4}{7}$. We can use the Giant **1** as a shortcut to compare these fractions.

a)   List the denominators that $\frac{3}{5}$ can have: 5, 10, 15, etc.

b)   List the denominators that $\frac{4}{7}$ can have: 7, 14, 21, etc.

c)   Circle the smallest denominator that $\frac{3}{5}$ and $\frac{4}{7}$ can share.

d)   Now use the idea of the Giant **1** to change the denominators of both fractions below to the denominator you need.

$$\frac{3}{5} \cdot \mathbb{1} = \frac{}{35} \qquad\qquad \frac{4}{7} \cdot \mathbb{1} = \frac{}{35}$$

e)   Compare the fractions. Which fraction is larger? Write a number sentence to show the relationship using an inequality symbol.

f)   Compare your work on this problem with the method in problem GO-39. Which method do you prefer?

GO-61. Use the Identity Property of Multiplication to change the following pairs of fractions to pairs with common denominators, then determine which of the two fractions is larger. Write an inequality statement (< or >) to compare $\frac{2}{3}$ and $\frac{5}{8}$:

Example: $\frac{2}{3} \cdot 1 = \frac{16}{24}$ and $\frac{5}{8} \cdot 1 = \frac{15}{24}$. Therefore, $\frac{2}{3} > \frac{5}{8}$.

Use the process above to compare the following fractions.

a) $\frac{7}{10}$ and $\frac{2}{3}$

b) $\frac{7}{10}$ and $\frac{3}{4}$

c) $\frac{4}{5}$ and $\frac{2}{3}$

GO-62. Hector is using radar to monitor speeds on a street near his school. He records the following speeds: 34, 37, 39, 40, 36, 35, 55, 40, 35, and 39.

a) Calculate the mean of these speeds.

b) Find the median.

c) Find the mode.

d) Hector wants to show that there is a speeding problem. Which measure of "average" would he use? Explain why.

e) What do you think the posted speed limit might be?

GO-63. Simplify each of the following expressions.

a) $4 - 3 \cdot (-7 + 4) \cdot 2$

b) $7 + 8 \cdot (8 - 40) + 1$

c) $(11 - 3 + (-4)) \div 3$

d) $\frac{23 + 13}{18 \div 3}$

GO-64. Write all the numbers between 1 and 40 that can be written as the sum of consecutive positive integers.

For example, $17 = 8 + 9$ and $26 = 5 + 6 + 7 + 8$.

a) Which numbers cannot be written this way?

b) Predict the next three numbers that are impossible to write in this way. How did you decide what they are?

GO-65. Practice mental math according to your teacher's directions. Explain in writing how you solved one of the problems.

GO-66. Here is a table that shows the three methods we used to find equivalent fractions. On the resource page your teacher gives you, show each of these methods to find the next three equivalent fractions for parts (a) through (c).

Item	Ratio Table	Giant **1**	Rectangular Model
$\frac{1}{2}$		$\frac{1}{2}\cdot\left[\frac{2}{2}\right]=\frac{2}{4}$ $\frac{1}{2}\cdot\left[\frac{3}{3}\right]=\frac{3}{6}$ $\frac{1}{2}\cdot\left[\frac{4}{4}\right]=\frac{4}{8}$	

Ratio Table:

1	2	3	4
2	4	6	8

Rectangular Model: $\frac{1}{2}$, $\frac{2}{4}$, $\frac{3}{6}$, $\frac{4}{8}$

a) $\frac{1}{3}$ b) $\frac{1}{4}$ c) $\frac{2}{5}$

GO-67. Assume Dr. Karydas sees 8 patients every two hours.

a) How many people does Dr. Karydas see in three hours? Solve by using a ratio table.

b) How many people can Dr. Karydas see in seven hours? Solve by using a ratio table.

c) How many patients can Dr. Karydas see in $1\frac{1}{2}$ hours? Solve by using the Identity Property of Multiplication (the Giant **1**).

d) How many patients can Dr. Karydas see in N hours?

e) If P is the number of patients Dr. Karydas sees in N hours, write an equation relating P and N.

GO-68. Check your answers to each part of the preceding problem by substituting the number of hours available as the value of N in the formula you just found. For example, if Dr. Karydas worked for five hours (N = 5), she would see $4(5) = 20$ patients.

GO-69.   The graph of the absolute value is interesting and
          different. Fill out the table at right and then plot the points
          on graph paper to get the graph of y = |x|. Since |-3| = 3,
          one of the points on the graph will be (-3, 3).

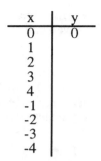

x	y
0	0
1	
2	
3	
4	
-1	
-2	
-3	
-4	

GO-70.   Play Fraction Blackout with Spinners C and D instead
          of Spinners A and B. Remember: the fraction in each
          part of the spinner is the value assigned to that sector,
          NOT the size of the sector. The spinner is not a pie chart.

GO-71.   Find the perimeter of the parallelogram at
          right by measuring. Measure sides to the
          nearest $\frac{1}{16}$ inch.

GO-72.   Use the Identity Property of Multiplication (the Giant **1**) or fraction strips to compare the
          following pairs of fractions and decide whether the first is less than (<), greater than (>), or
          equal to (=) the second. If you use fraction strips, draw an accurate picture.

   a) $\frac{4}{5} \cdot \mathbb{1} = \frac{}{20}$ and $\frac{3}{4} \cdot \mathbb{1} = \frac{}{20}$ b) $\frac{3}{8}$ and $\frac{2}{3}$

   c) $\frac{2}{5}$ and $\frac{3}{7}$ d) $\frac{10}{12}$ and $\frac{7}{9}$

   e)   What is the smallest common denominator for part (d)?

GO-73.   Using your fraction bars, replace each variable to make the equations true.

   a) $\frac{1}{12} = \frac{1}{4} - M$ b) $\frac{2}{3} = \frac{3}{4} - N$ c) $\frac{1}{8} = \frac{1}{2} - P$

   d) $\frac{1}{6} = \frac{2}{3} - Q$ e) $\frac{3}{4} = \frac{7}{8} - R$ f) $\frac{3}{12} = \frac{2}{3} - T$

GO-74.   **Diamond Problems** Complete the Diamond Problems below.

Product

Sum

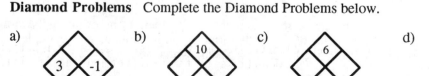

a)   b)   c)   d)

GO-75. Use your fraction-decimal-percent grid. Write an equation that lists equivalent expressions for the shaded area in each box. Be sure you name at least one fraction, one decimal, and one percent for each problem.

a)

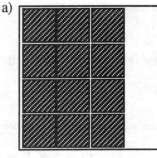

b)

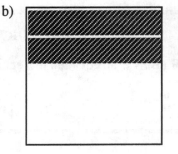

c)

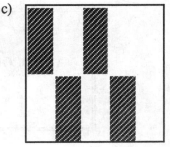

GO-76. Using a straightedge, carefully draw **your initials** with straight line letters. Measure the length of each line segment to the nearest sixteenth of an inch. Find the "length" of your initials by adding all the line segments. You may want to use graph paper. An example is shown at right.

GO-77. Which fraction represents 6%?

(A) $\frac{60}{100}$ (B) $\frac{6}{1000}$ (C) $\frac{6}{10}$ (D) $\frac{6}{100}$

GO-78. Find the perimeter of the white part of the diagram at right.

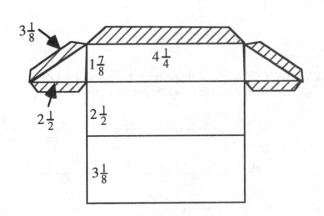

GO-79. Exchange your work from problem GO-76 with your partner. Check your partner's measurements. Also check the calculation of the total length of your partner's initials. When you have completed this task, write "checked by" and sign your name.

GO-80. In this chapter we have been working with equivalent fractions that represent the same amount. Technically, we have been working with **proportions**.

> ### PROPORTION
>
> A **PROPORTION** is an equation that states that two fractions are equal.
>
> $$\frac{3}{8} = \frac{6}{16} \qquad\qquad \frac{4}{12} = \frac{6}{18} \qquad\qquad \frac{2}{3} = \frac{x}{30}$$

a) Use the Identity Property of Multiplication (Giant **1**) to show that $\frac{2}{3} = \frac{8}{12}$ is a proportion. Write your work in the space to the right of the double-lined box in your Tool Kit.

b) Find a value of x so that $\frac{x}{6} = \frac{2}{3}$ is a proportion.

c) Find a value of y so that $\frac{10}{y} = \frac{2}{3}$ is a proportion.

GO-81. Use a ratio table, a rectangular model, or the Identity Property of Multiplication (Giant **1**) to decide which of the following ratio pairs could form a correct proportion. Be sure to show your work.

a) $\frac{6}{16}, \frac{3}{8}$ b) $\frac{5}{9}, \frac{4}{8}$ c) $\frac{4}{6}, \frac{6}{9}$ d) $\frac{6}{10}, \frac{9}{15}$

GO-82. Complete these ratio tables which convert quantities. In the last column, write an appropriate variable expression.

a)
Minutes	1	4	6		M
Seconds		240		12	

b)
Hours	1	2	10		H
Minutes	60			1440	

c)
Hours	1	4	56		H
Seconds				72,000	

d) For the problems above, write the three equations which relate seconds (S), minutes (M), and hours (H). For example, from (a) you will see S = 60M.
Now write the other two equations.

GO-83.   Jeri was buying detergent for washing dishes at home. She knew that the last 12 ounce bottle she bought lasted about 6 weeks.

a)   Assuming that her family generally uses detergent at the same rate, fill in the following table.

Ounces of Detergent	12	8	30	
Number of Weeks	6			9

b)   Use the table above to write an equation relating D (the number of ounces of detergent) and W (the number of weeks the detergent will last)

c)   Use graph paper to draw a graph relating D and W. The horizontal axis should represent the number of ounces of detergent, and the vertical axis should represent the number of weeks the detergent will last. To help you start, if you have 0 ounces of detergent, it will last 0 weeks, so (0, 0) is one of the points on your graph.

GO-84.   When Harris returned from Canada he still had 96 Canadian dollars (C). At the time, each U.S. dollar (A) was worth $1.50 in Canadian dollars. Use ratios to find the value of his Canadian dollars in U.S. dollars.

a)   Use a ratio table to solve the problem.

U.S. dollars	$1.00		$8.00		$32.00	
Canadian dollars	$1.50	$3.00		$24.00		$96.00

b)   Suppose Harris had C Canadian dollars and converted them to A U.S. dollars. Write an equation that expresses A in terms of C.

GO-85.   Tim earns $6.25 per hour at Robert's Run-Inn Restaurant. He can only work four hours a day at the restaurant. If he actually makes $5 per hour after taxes are deducted, how many days will it take him to earn $325 to buy a CD player? Solve the problem using either a ratio table or a Giant 1 to solve the proportion.

GO-86.   Use your fraction bars to find the answer to these division problems.

a)   How many $\frac{1}{12}$s are in $\frac{2}{3}$?

b)   How many $\frac{1}{8}$s are in $\frac{3}{4}$?

c)   How many $\frac{1}{6}$s are in $\frac{2}{3}$?

d)   How many $\frac{1}{8}$s are in $\frac{1}{2}$?

e)   How many $\frac{1}{6}$s are in $\frac{4}{4}$?

GO-87.   Find the perimeter and area of the figure at right. All dimensions are given in feet. Make sure you <u>show</u> <u>all</u> <u>subproblems</u>. Re-draw this figure and sketch the rectangles you will use for the subproblems.

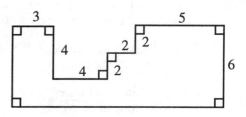

GO-88.   **Algebra Puzzles** Write three pairs of numbers that make each equation true. For each equation, choose at least one value of x that is a mixed number.

a) $y = x + 9$ b) $y = x - 9$

c) $y = 2x - 1$ d) $y = 6x - 3$

GO-89.   Simplify each expression.

a) $\dfrac{4 + 8 \cdot 2}{12 \div 2 - 1}$ b) $3 \cdot (9 - 6) + 3 + 2 \cdot 5$

c) $3 \cdot (3 + 6) + 3 \cdot 8$ d) $\dfrac{35 \div 7 \cdot 5}{5 \cdot (3 + 2)}$

GO-90.   We often use letters or variables the same way we use blanks in ratio tables.

4	x	8
10	15	20

a)   Find what x would be in this ratio table.

b)   Since the ratios are equal, write a proportion using x from the table above.

GO-91.   Five members of the school band were planning the annual band dinner and concert fund-raiser. Last year they found that 16 pounds of spaghetti feeds 40 people. This year they hope to feed 160 people in the cafeteria and 360 more in the gym. Decide how much spaghetti they will need in each location.

a)   Answer this question by using a ratio table.

b)   Answer this question by using a Giant **1**.

GO-92. Mai found she needed 20 ounces of noodles to feed 6 people. She needed to find how many ounces of noodles would be needed to feed 9 people.

a) Solve the problem using a ratio table.

People	6	9	12
Ounces of Noodles	20	x	40

b) If Mai were buying noodles for 45 people, how many ounces of noodles would she need to buy?

GO-93. Copy and complete the equivalent fraction ratio table.

N	6	12	30			2
D	15			150	10	

a) Write any three fraction ratios from the table as proportions.

b) Write an equation that relates N and D.

GO-94. Patricia Garcia was reading a story to her sister, Ana, about a kindly giant who lived in a very cold place. Ana felt sorry for the giant and wanted to make him a quilt just like hers (only bigger, of course). Ana's quilt is 3744 square inches and took 104 hours to make. Ana wants the giant quilt to be 9360 square inches. If she makes the giant quilt at the same rate at which she made her quilt, how long will it take to make it?

a) How many hours will it take to make the quilt? How many days?

b) How much bigger is the giant's quilt than Ana's?

c) Describe the method you used to solve this problem.

GO-95. The dog chewed up part of Marco's homework paper so that all that was left of the first problem was $\frac{4}{33} = \frac{\square}{1782}$. What was the missing numerator?

GO-96. We are going to arrange fractions along a number line.

a) Draw a number line from 0 to 1 like the one below.

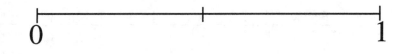

b) Mentally sort the fractions below into three groups: closest to 0, closest to $\frac{1}{2}$, and closest to 1.

$$\frac{14}{8} \quad \frac{3}{16} \quad \frac{3}{8} \quad \frac{16}{16} \quad \frac{1}{4} \quad \frac{1}{8} \quad \frac{3}{4} \quad \frac{7}{8}$$

c) Now write the fractions on the number line where they belong. You may need to find a common denominator to compare fractions.

GO-97. Use a ruler to draw a line segment with each of the following lengths. Draw the four line segments end-to-end so they make one straight line. Be sure to mark the starting and stopping place for each line segment. Start near the left edge of your paper.

a) $3\frac{3}{8}$ inches   b) $2\frac{3}{16}$ inches   c) $1\frac{3}{4}$ inches   d) $\frac{1}{2}$ inches

e) Add to find the total length of the line segment composed of parts (a) and (b). Check your work by measuring.

f) Add, then measure to check the total length of the line segments composed of parts (c) and (d).

g) Find the total length of the line segments in parts (b), (c), and (d).

h) Find the total length of all four line segments by adding the fractions. You may use your fraction bars. Check your work by measuring.

GO-98. Complete these tables which convert quantities:

a)

feet	1	4	6		f
inches		48		60	

b)

miles	1	2	10		m
feet	5280			58,080	

c)

yards	1	4	56		y
feet	3			333	

GO-99.   To find her usual bedtime, Zoe kept a record of what time she went to bed. These are
          the times she recorded: 9:30 p.m., 10:30 p.m., 10:00 p.m., 9:00 p.m., 11:00 p.m.,
          9:00 p.m., 9:30 p.m., 10:00 p.m., 11:00 p.m., and 9:00 p.m.

          a)   Find the mode of Zoe's bedtimes.

          b)   Find the median.

          c)   When you calculate the mean, what values will you use for
                9:30 p.m. and 10:30 p.m.?

          d)   Calculate the mean.

          e)   If Zoe wants to convince her parents that she usually goes to bed early and should be
                allowed to stay up late this Friday, which measure of central tendency will she use?
                Explain.

GO-100.   Use your fraction bars to solve these mixed practice problems:

          a) $\frac{11}{12} = W + Y$ b) $\frac{3}{8} = \frac{3}{6} - K$ c) $\frac{1}{4} = N - \frac{7}{12}$

          d)   How many groups of two-thirds are in $3\frac{2}{3}$?

          e)   How many $\frac{1}{12}$s are in $1\frac{1}{4}$?

GO-101.   The Garcias plan to carpet 1962 square feet of their
          house. Carpet is sold by the square yard, and the
          carpet Maria Garcia has chosen costs $15.00 per
          square yard.

          a)   How many square yards are there in the
                Garcias' house? Remember that one square
                yard is equal to nine square feet.

          b)   How much will it cost for the Garcias to
                carpet their house?

GO-102. Victor and Hugo were shooting baskets. Hugo made 6 of his 10 shots. Victor made 12 out of 15 shots. Who is the better shooter?

a) Answer this question by using a ratio table.

b) Answer this question using a Giant **1**.

c) Answer this question using a proportion.

GO-103. **Algebra Puzzles** Write three ordered pairs that make each of the following equations true. Use at least one fraction greater than one for x in each equation.

a) y = -2x + 1

b) y = -2x – 1

GO-104. Simplify each expression.

a) $2 \cdot (3 \cdot 4 + 8) + 6 \cdot 2$

b) $7 + 5 \cdot (2 \cdot 3 + 6) \cdot 2 + 7$

c) $(4 \cdot 9) - (6 \cdot 3) \cdot 2 + 4$

d) $8 + 7 \cdot (6 + 18 \div 3) + 28 \div 2$

GO-105.

Chapter Summary It is time to summarize and review what you have learned in this chapter.

a) Go back and read problem GO-57. Explain how to find an equivalent fraction for $\frac{5}{7}$ using all three models.

b) Explain how to compare two fractions.

GO-106. **Self Evaluation** When you finish a chapter, you need to reflect on how well you have learned the material. One way to check your understanding at the end of a chapter is to try a problem from each objective and then evaluate your confidence with that objective. Try these five problems which match the five objectives from this chapter.

a) Find the equivalent fraction: $\frac{2}{5} = \frac{8}{x}$.

b) Show how to use the Giant **1** to show $\frac{3}{4} = \frac{15}{20}$.

c) Complete this ratio table.

x	6		30
y	3	12	

d) Write an equation based on the ratio table in (c) that relates y to x.

e) Your teacher will tell your class the answers to the four questions in parts (a) through (d). After you check your answers, write the objective name and then use the scale described below. For example, you might write, "Equivalent fraction ability = 3." The other objectives would be "Giant **1**," "ratio tables," and "writing equations from ratio tables."

On a scale of 1 through 5, evaluate your understanding of the objective.

1 = I don't understand this skill.
2 = I do not understand it well.
3 = I usually understand this idea, but I might need a little more practice.
4 = I understand this topic quite well.
5 = Bring on the quiz! I understand this idea very well.

GO-107. Draw a rectangle, use vertical lines, and shade $\frac{3}{5}$. Then draw in the number of horizontal lines needed to show multiplication by $\frac{4}{4}$.

a) What fraction now represents the shaded part?

b) The shaded part is also represented by $\frac{3}{5}$. Write an equation to show the relationship between the two representations.

c) Copy and complete this table to verify the relationship you wrote in part (b).

Numerator	3	6	9	
Denominator	5			20

GO-108. **Diamond Problems** Complete the Diamond Problems below.

Product

Sum

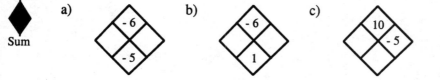

a) b) c) d)

GO-109. Complete these ratio tables.

a)

Hours	1		7		13	H
Pay	$5.25	$10.50		$52.50		

b) Write the equation which relates H, hours worked, and P, pay received.

c)

Sodas	2		5		15	S
Cost	$0.90	$1.35		$2.70		

d) Write the equation which relates S, the number of sodas, and C, their cost.

GO-110. Fill in the ratio table to find other fractions equivalent to $\frac{3}{8}$.

N	3	6			33	-3	
D	8		80	1600			-16

GO-111. Terry thinks he is a better basketball shooter than Larry because he made 17 out of 30 shots while Larry only made 12 out of 20 shots. Use the method of your choice to determine who is the better shooter.

GO-112. Jawbreakers are 3 for $0.15.

a) Fill in the following ratio table:

Number	1	2	3		143	N
Cost			$0.15	$0.25		

b) How much will 213 jawbreakers cost?

GO-113.   Use your fraction bars to answer the following questions.

   a)   How many groups of $\frac{5}{12}$s are in $\frac{5}{6}$?

   b)   How many groups of $\frac{3}{8}$s are in $\frac{3}{4}$?

   c)   How many one-halves are in $\frac{3}{4}$?

   d)   How many one-sixths are in $\frac{5}{12}$?

   e)   How many one-thirds are in $1\frac{1}{2}$?

GO-114.   While Mrs. Poppington was visiting the historic
           battleground at Gettysburg, she began talking to the
           workmen who were replacing the sod in a park near
           the visitor's center. The part of the lawn being
           replaced is shown in the diagram at right.
           (Measurements are in yards. The diagram is not
           drawn to scale, but all corners are right angles.)

   a)   Use your ruler to make a scale drawing of the park. Let $\frac{1}{4}$ inch equal 1 yard.

   b)   How many square yards of sod will be needed?

   c)   At $2.43 a square yard, how much will the sod cost?

   d)   The area will be surrounded by a temporary fence which costs $0.25 per <u>linear foot</u>.
        How many <u>feet</u> will be needed, and how much will it cost?

   e)   How much will it cost to replace the sod?

GO-115.   Write each line length shown below using mixed numbers.

   a)   b)

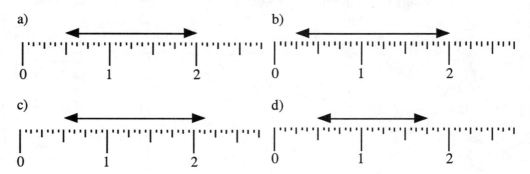

   c)   d)

GO-116. Every summer, Jacque's mother takes him to see her family in Luxembourg. The day he arrives, his grandfather measures him. The table at right gives his height (in centimeters) each year. Plot Jacque's growth on graph paper. The horizontal axis should be his age, and the vertical axis should be his height. On the horizontal axis use one space for each year of age; on the vertical axis use one space for each 10 centimeters of height.

Age (years)	Height (cm)
1	61
2	89
3	96
4	99
5	103
6	107
7	112
8	119
9	126
10	134
11	142
12	151
13	160
14	169
15	177
16	182

GO-117. It costs $21 to buy enough potato salad to feed 40 people. How much will it cost to buy enough potato salad for 180 people? Set up a ratio table to answer the question.

GO-118. Take your pulse for 10 seconds. Remember to use your index and middle fingers, not your thumb. Assume that your pulse rate will be fairly constant over the time periods mentioned below. Use a ratio table or the Identity Property of Multiplication (the Giant **1**) to solve each part.

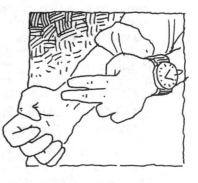

a) How many times does your heart beat in 10 seconds?

b) 30 seconds?   c) 60 seconds?   d) 5 minutes?

e) 60 minutes?   f) 24 hours?

GO-119. Find the perimeter and area of the figure at right. All dimensions given are in meters. Make sure you show all subproblems.

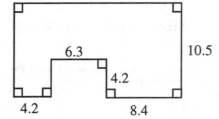

GO-120. Using your fraction bars, replace each variable to make the equations true.

a) $\frac{1}{3} = \frac{1}{4} + H$

b) $\frac{2}{3} = \frac{1}{2} + L$

c) $\frac{5}{8} = \frac{1}{4} + W$

d) $\frac{5}{6} = Q + \frac{1}{3}$

e) $\frac{3}{4} = \frac{3}{8} + B$

f) $\frac{7}{8} = D + \frac{5}{12}$

GO-121. For which equation is (3, 6) a solution?

(A) $3x = y$ (B) $x - y = 3$ (C) $x + y = 9$ (D) $\frac{x}{y} = 2$

GO-122. **What We Have Done in This Chapter**

Below is a list of the Tool Kit entries from this chapter.

- GO-1   Ratios
- GO-7   Mixed Numbers and Fractions Greater Than One
- GO-14   Equivalent Fractions
- GO-41   Inequality Symbols
- GO-52   Identity Property of Multiplication (also GO-61)
- GO-80   Proportions

Review all the entries and read the notes you made in your Tool Kit. Make a list of any questions, terms, or notes you do not understand. Ask your partner or study team members for help. If anything is still unclear, ask your teacher.

GLOSSARY

absolute value: (| |) The distance of a number from zero. It is always non-negative. (56)

acute angle: An angle with a measure of less than 90°. (101)

acute triangle: A triangle with all three angle measures less than 90°. (101)

addition: (+) An operation that tells how many things there are when two sets are combined. The result is the number of objects in the two sets together, called a sum. In arithmetic, the word "object" usually means "number." (38, 224)

adjacent angles: Angles which share a common side and vertex but no common interior points. (281)

algebra: A branch of mathematics that uses variables to generalize the rules of numbers and numerical operations.

algebraic expression: Variables and constants, possibly joined by operations. Examples: $3x$ or $2x + 4$ (78)

algorithm: A fixed rule for carrying out a mathematical procedure. Example: To find the average of a set of values, find their sum and divide by the number of values.

altitude of a triangle (height): The perpendicular distance from a vertex to the opposite side (or its extension) of a triangle.

angle: A geometric figure made up of two rays or line segments that have the same endpoint. (101)

arc: The portion of a circle between two points on a circle.

area: The measure in square units of the interior region of a plane figure or the surface of a three dimensional figure. (103)

area of triangle: To find the area of a triangle, multiply the length of the base by the height and divide by two. $A = \frac{1}{2} bh$ (117)

area of a circle: $A = \pi r^2$, where r is the length of the radius of the circle. See area. (331)

associative property for addition: Changing the grouping of the numbers does not change the result in addition. Example: $(5 + 3) + 7 = 5 + (3 + 7)$ (308)

associative property for multiplication: Changing the grouping of the numbers does not change the result in multiplication. Example: $(5 \cdot 3) \cdot 2 = 5 \cdot (3 \cdot 2)$ (308)

average (mean): The sum of given numbers divided by the number of numbers used in computing the sum. Example: The average of 1, 4, and 10 is $(1 + 4 + 10) \div 3 = 5$. (11)

axis (pl. axes): A number line which can be used to indicate a position of a point, based on its coordinates. (43)

base of an exponent: The number used as the factor in an exponential expression. Example: $5^2 = 5 \cdot 5$. 5 is the base.

base: For a triangle, the base may be any side, although usually it is the bottom one. For a trapezoid, the two parallel sides are the bases. For a cylinder or prism, either one of the two congruent parallel faces may be the base while for a pyramid or cone, the base is the (flat) face which does not contain the vertex (where all the sides come together). (101, 108, 117)

biased question: A question is biased if it makes assumptions about the person being questioned or if it makes one answer seem better than another. (378)

bimodal: A set of numbers that has two modes.

causality: When one event causes another to occur. (396)

certainty: When an event will definitely happen. The probability of a certain event is 1. (363)

center: (or center point) The point equidistant from all points on a circle. (323)

central angle: An angle whose vertex is the center of a circle.

chord: A line segment that connects two points on a circle.

circle: The set of all points in two dimensions that are the same distance r from a fixed point P. The fixed point P is called the center of the circle and the distance r is called the radius. (101, 323)

circumference: The distance around the outside of a circle. You can calculate circumference by multiplying π by the length of the diameter. $C = \pi d = 2\pi r$. (327)

closed option: A question with a limited number of possible answers. (383)

coefficient (numerical): The numeral part of a term, such as 6 in 6x.

combining like terms: When working with an expression, terms with the same variables (with the same exponents) can be combined into one quantity. Numbers are combined by addition and subtraction. Example: $3x^2 + 2y + 6 + 4y - 2x^2 = x^2 + 6y + 6$. (298)

common: Shared.

common factor: A common term factor: (1) in arithmetic, the integers multiplied are called factors; (2) in algebra, a monomial or polynomial that is a factor of a polynomial. For example: $10x + 15 = 5 \cdot 2x + 5 \cdot 3 = 5(2x + 3)$. Five is the common factor.

common multiple: A number that is a multiple of the two or more numbers. Example: 24 and 48 are common multiples of 3 and 8. (186)

commutative property: The property of an operation such that changing the order of the numbers does not change the result of the operation. Examples: $3 \cdot 4 = 4 \cdot 3$ or $7 + 8 = 8 + 7$ (308)

complementary angles: Two angles whose sum is 90°. (281)

complementary probabilities: Two probabilities are complementary if their sum is one.

complex fraction: A fraction with a fraction in the numerator and/or the denominator. (254)

composite figure: A shape made of several simpler figures. (121)

composite number: A number with more than two factors.

compound events: A combination of simple events.

congruent: Figures which have the same size and shape. (106)

conjecture: An educated guess, based on data, patterns, and data. Scientists use the term hypothesis. (96)

consecutive: In order. Example: 8, 9,10 are consecutive numbers. (315)

constant: A numerical term which does not change.

coordinate grid (system): A two dimensional system formed by two perpendicular number lines that intersect at their zero points. The location of a point is given by first stating the horizontal location (x) and then the vertical location (y), written as an ordered pair, (x, y). (↖)

correlation: A measure of interdependence of two sets of data. (395)

cross multiplication: A way to find a missing numerator or denominator in equivalent fractions by multiplying diagonally across the equal sign to get an equivalent equation without fractions. Example: In $\frac{a}{b} = \frac{c}{d}$, after cross multiplication the equation would be ad = bc. (183)

cube: A rectangular prism with 6 congruent faces, all squares.

cubic unit: A cube each of whose edges measures 1 unit in length. Volume is measured in cubic units..

cylinder: Commonly, a three dimensional object with two circular, congruent, and parallel bases. (344)

decimal point: The dot separating the ones and tenths places in a decimal number.

denominator: The lower part of a fraction which tells into how many equal parts the whole is divided. (156)

dependent events: Two events are dependent if the outcome of the first event affects the outcome of the second event. (366)

diagonal: A segment that joins two vertices of a polygon and is not one of the sides. (101)

diameter: A line segment that has its endpoints on the circle and passes through the center. The longest chord in a circle. (323)

difference: The answer to a subtraction problem. (73)

digit: One of the ten numerals: 0, 1, 2, 3, 4, 5, 6, 7, 8, 9.

distributive property: For any a, b, and c, a (b + c) = ab + ac. Example: 10(7 + 2) = 10·7 + 10·2 (303)

dividend: A quantity to be divided. See: divisor.

divisible: A number is divisible by another if their remainder is zero.

division: The inverse operation to multiplication The operation which creates equal groups. (29, 183, 248, 263)

divisor: The quantity by which another quantity is to be divided. dividend ÷ divisor = quotient

edge: The line segment where two faces of a solid figure meet.

endpoint: Either of the two points which mark the ends of a line segment.

equal: Having the same value. (4)

equal ratios: Two equivalent fractions; a proportion. (166)

equation: A mathematical sentence relating two mathematical expressions with an equal sign (=). (4)

equilateral triangle: A triangle with all three sides the same length. (101)

equivalent: Naming the same amount with a different name. (149)

evaluate (an expression): To evaluate an expression, substitute the value(s) given for the variable(s) and perform the operations according to the order of operations. (298)

even number: A whole number divisible by two with no remainder.

event: One or more results of an experiment. (363)

experimental probability: Probability based upon the results of an experiment.
$$P(\text{event}) = \frac{\text{\# of times an event occurs}}{\text{\# of times the experiment took place}} \quad (365)$$

exponent: In the expression 2^5, 5 is called the exponent. The exponent indicates how many times to use the base as a multiplier.

expression: See algebraic expression. (78)

face: A polygonal region of a three-dimensional figure. (337)

factor: When two or more numbers are multiplied, each of the numbers multiplied is a factor of the product.

factored form: Use the distributive property to change from a sum to a product. Example: 10x + 15 = 5(2x + 3)

formula: An equation that shows a mathematical relationship.

fraction: A number expressed in the form $\frac{a}{b}$ where a and b are whole numbers, b $\neq$ zero. (9)

frequency: The number of times something occurs in an interval or in a data set.

graph: A visual display of information in an organized manner. (43)

greatest common factor (GCF): The largest number which will divide evenly into two or more numbers. Example: 6 is the greatest common factor of 12 and 18.

guess and check table: A problem solving strategy in which you begin by making a guess and then check whether or not your answer is correct. In the process of checking, you gain information about how close your guess might be and make adjustments to your guess. Being organized is crucial to the success of this method, as well as writing a usable table. Guess and check leads to writing equations to represent word problems. (70)

height (altitude): The perpendicular distance between 2 bases, or a vertex and a base. See altitude. (105, 108, 117)

hexagon: A polygon with six sides. (101)

horizontal: Parallel to the horizon. The x-axis in a coordinate grid. (43)

identity property of addition: Zero is the identity for addition: It does not change the value of a number when added to the number. (405)

identity property of multiplication: One is the identity element for multiplication. Multiplying by one does not change the value of a number. (159)

impossibility: An event with a probability of zero. (363)

independent events: Two events are independent if the outcome of the first event does not depend on the outcome of the second event. (366)

inequality: A mathematical sentence which compares two quantities, showing they are not the same. The symbols used may be: < (less than), > (greater than), to), or $\neq$ (not equal to). (157)

integers: The set of numbers { . . ., -3, -2, -1, 0, 1, 2, 3,... } (27)

interval: A set of numbers between two given numbers.

irrational numbers: Numbers that can not be written as the ratio of two integers.

inverse operations: An operation that undoes another operation. Example: multiplication is the inverse operation for division. (56)

isosceles triangle: A triangle with at least two sides equal in length. (101)

least common multiple (LCM): The smallest common multiple of set of two or more numbers. Example: the least common multiple of 4 and 6 is 12. (187)

like terms: Terms that have the same variable part and corresponding exponent. 5 and 19 are like terms, 3xy and 5xy are like terms, $6x^2$ and $-3x^2$ are like terms. (298)

line: An infinite set of points forming a straight path extending in two directions.

line segment: A part of a line with endpoints. (101)

linear equation: An equation whose graph is a line, generated by an equation with a linear expression in it.

linear expression: An expression in the form of ax + b, where a and b are numbers.

lowest common denominator (LCD): The smallest common multiple of the denominators of two or more fractions. Example: The LCD of $\frac{5}{12}$ and $\frac{3}{8}$ is 24. (223)

mean: A measure of central tendency often referred to as the average. See average. (11)

measure of central tendency: Mean, median, and mode are all measures of central tendency, reflecting specific statistical information about a set of data. (20)

median: The middle number of a set of ordered data. If there is no distinct middle, the average of the two middle numbers is the median. (15)

mode: The number or numbers that show up the most in a set of data. There can be more than one mode. (11)

midpoint: The point on a line segment that divides the line segment into two congruent line segments.

mixed number (fraction): A number with an integer component and a fraction component. Example: $2\frac{3}{4}$ (147)

multiple: The product of a whole number and any other (non-zero) whole number. Example: 15 is a multiple of five.

multiplication: An operation which reflects repeated addition. Example: $3 \cdot 4 = 4 + 4 + 4$. (49, 236, 261)

natural numbers: The counting numbers beginning with 1. Example: 1, 2, 3...

negative numbers: Numbers which are less than zero, designated with a − sign. (27)

negative correlation: A relationship between two sets of variables in which one generally increases as the other decreases. (396)

net: A two dimensional one-piece plan which can be folded into a three dimensional shape. (347)

number line: A diagram representing all real numbers as points on a line. (27)

numeral: An expression (which is not a variable) that names a particular number.

numerator: The number above the bar in a fraction which tells the number of parts in relationship to the number of parts in the whole.

numerical order: To write numbers from smallest to largest. (15)

obtuse angle: An angle greater than 90° and less than 180˚. (101)

octagon: A polygon with eight sides. (101)

odd number: A whole number which can not be evenly divided by 2.

open option: A question which allows free response. (383)

operation: In mathematics, addition, subtraction, multiplication, division, raising to a power and taking a root are operations. (72)

order of operations: Rules which define in what sequence operations will be completed when an expression is presented for evaluation. Expressions inside parentheses are evaluated first, then multiplication or division (left to right) followed by addition and subtraction (left to right). (81)

origin: The point assigned to zero on the number line or the point where the x- and y-axes intersect in a coordinate system. (43)

ordered pair: A pair of numbers (a, b) used to indicate a position on a coordinate plane. The first number indicates the horizontal coordinate; the second number indicates the vertical coordinate. Syn: coordinate. (43)

outcome: Possible results in an experiment or consequence of an action. (363)

parallel: ($\parallel$) Two lines which never intersect and are the same distance apart are said to be parallel. (101)

parallelogram: A quadrilateral with opposite sides parallel. (101)

pentagon: A polygon with five sides. (101)

percent: (%) A ratio that compares a number to 100. (75, 199)

perfect square: The product of an integer times itself gives a perfect square. Example: 1, 4, and 9 are perfect squares because $1 = 1 \cdot 1$; $4 = 2 \cdot 2$; $9 = 3 \cdot 3$; $16 = 4 \cdot 4$...

perimeter: The distance around a figure on a flat surface. (62)

perpendicular: ($\perp$) Lines, segments, or rays that intersect to form right angles. (101)

pi (π): The ratio of a circle's circumference to its diameter. An irrational number, it is common to use the approximation of 3.14 or $\frac{22}{7}$ if you are not using a scientific calculator with a π key. (326)

place value: The value of a position of a digit in a number.

plane: A flat surface that extends infinitely in all directions. It has no thickness.

point: An exact location in space. In two dimensions, an ordered pair specifies a point in a coordinate plane. (43)

poll: (verb) To ask questions in a survey or election, (noun) a survey. (373)

polygon: A two dimensional closed figure with straight line segments connected end to end. The segments may not cross. Examples: triangle or quadrilateral. (101)

polyhedron: A three dimensional figure in which all surfaces are polygons.

population: A collection of objects or group of people about whom information is gathered. (388)

power(exponent): See exponent.

positive correlation: A relationship between two sets of variables in which one generally increases as the other increases. (395)

positive numbers: Numbers that a greater than zero.

prime: A number with exactly two factors. Examples: 2, 3, 5, 7...

prime factorization: The expression of a number as the product of prime factors.

prism: A 3 dimensional figure composed of polygonal faces and two parallel, congruent faces called bases, no holes are permitted in the solid. The remaining faces are parallelograms (or other special quadrilaterals). A prism is named for the shape of its base. (337)

probability: The chance of an event happening. When the outcomes are equally likely, it equals the number of event outcomes divided by the total number of outcomes. Example: when rolling a number cube, the probability that you will roll a $3 = \dfrac{1 \text{ way}}{6 \text{ possible outcomes}} = \dfrac{1}{6}$. (363)

product (·): Result of multiplying. Example: 72 is the product of 8 · 9. (83)

proportion: Two equivalent ratios. Example: $\dfrac{1}{3} = \dfrac{3}{9}$ (166)

quadrants: The four sections of a coordinate grid.

quadrilateral: A polygon with four sides. (101)

quotient: The result of a division problem.

radius: (plural: **radii**) The distance from the center to a point on the circle. (323)

random sample: A sample in which each item in the population or sample space has an equal chance of being selected. (388)

range: In statistics, the difference between the least and greatest pieces of data. (11)

rate: A ratio comparing two quantities, often a comparison of time. Example: miles per hour.

ratio: A comparison of two numbers which can indicate division. It can be written three ways: 2 boys to 5 girls, 2 boys : 5 girls, or $\dfrac{2 \text{ boys}}{5 \text{ girls}}$. (145)

rational number: A number that can be written in the form $\dfrac{a}{b}$ with a and b integers and b ≠ zero.

ray: A portion of a line that has one endpoint and extends forever in one direction. (101)

real numbers: The set of rational and irrational numbers. (All the numbers on the number line.)

reciprocals: Two numbers which have a product of 1. Example: 2 and $\frac{1}{2}$ are reciprocals of each other. (250)

rectangle: A quadrilateral with four right angles. Its two pairs of opposite sides are parallel and congruent. (101)

reduce: To put a fraction into simplest form. (240)

regular polygon: A polygon in which all sides are congruent and all angles have the same measure. (101)

representative sample: A subset (group) of a given population with the same characteristics as the population. (388)

rhombus: A quadrilateral with four congruent sides. (101)

right angle: An angle with a measure of 90°. (101)

right triangle: A triangle with one right angle in it. (101)

root: A number that can be used as a factor a given number of times. Example: The square root of 16 is 4 because $4 \cdot 4 = 16$. $\sqrt{16} = 4$

sample: A subgroup selected from a larger group. (388)

sample space: The set of all possible outcomes from which a sample is taken, often the same as the population. (363)

scale (scaling): An arrangement of numbers in uniform intervals. (25)

scalene triangle: A triangle with no two sides of equal length. (101)

scatter plot: Two related sets of data graphed as points; often in a coordinate plane. *See positive and negative correlation.* (395)

scientific notation: A method of writing very large or very small numbers as a product of a power of ten and a number greater than or equal to one and less than 10. Example: $124,500 = 1.245 \cdot 10^5$

sector: A part of the interior of a circle bounded by two radii and the arc between their endpoints. (345)

semi-circle: Half of a circle. (343)

set: A collection of items. (248)

similar figures: Figures which are similar have the same shape but not necessarily the same size; the lengths of the corresponding sides are proportional to one another; the corresponding angles are congruent. (205)

simplest form of a fraction: A fraction whose numerator and denominator have no common factor greater than one. (240)

simplify: To combine like terms; to express the quantity using as few symbols as possible; to put a fraction in lowest terms. (240, 298)

slope: A way to specify the steepness of a line defined as the ratio of the vertical distance divided by the horizontal distance between any two points on the line.

solution: Any value for a variable that makes an equation true. (20)

square: A quadrilateral with four congruent sides and four right angles. (101)

square number: Any number which is the product of two identical whole numbers. (example: $1 \cdot 1 = 1$, $2 \cdot 2 = 4$, $3 \cdot 3 = 9$ ...)

square root: See root.

square measure: The units used to describe the measure of an area in the form of 1 x 1 unit squares. (103)

stem and leaf plot: A frequency distribution made by arranging the data. (17)

straight angle: A 180° angle. (274)

subproblems: A problem solving strategy which breaks a problem into smaller parts which must be solved in order to solve the original, complex problem. (121)

substitution: Replacing one symbol by another (a number, a variable, or other algebraic expression) without changing the value of the expression. (55)

subtraction (-): An operation that gives the difference between two numbers. (73, 224)

sum: An answer to a addition problem. (38)

supplementary angles: Two angles whose measurements give a sum of 180°. (281)

surface area: The total area of all faces and bases of a polyhedron, cylinder, cone, or pyramids. (348)

survey: (verb) To ask questions in a survey or election, (noun) a survey. *Syn: poll* (383)

term: Each part of the expression separated by addition or subtraction signs is a term. (81, 298)

theoretical probability: A probability calculated using the formula.
$$P = \frac{\text{\# of favorable outcomes}}{\text{\# of equally likely possible outcomes}} \quad (365)$$

tick mark: An indicator that a number line has been divided into intervals of equal length.

trimodel: A set of data that has three modes.

trapezoid: A quadrilateral with exactly one pair of parallel sides. (101)

triangle: A polygon with three sides. (101)

unit fraction: A fraction with a numerator of one.

unit price: The cost of one item or one measure of an item. Example: cost for one pound or one gallon. (201)

unit rate: A rate with a denominator of one. (202)

units digit: The numeral in the ones place.

variable: A symbol or letter that stands for a number. (20)

vertex: The point at which two rays, line segments, or lines meet. (101)

vertical: At right angles to the horizon. In a coordinate grid, the y axis runs vertically. (43)

vertical angles: The angles opposite each other when two lines intersect. (101)

volume: The number of cubic units inside a three dimensional object. (336)

x-axis: The horizontal number line on a coordinate grid. (43)

x-intercepts: The point(s) where a graph intersects the x-axis. The x-intercept always has coordinates (x, 0).

y-axis: The vertical number line on a coordinate grid. (43)

y-intercepts: The point(s) where a graph intersects the y-axis. The y-intercept always has coordinates (0, y).

INDEX

Chapter Prefixes

Many of the page numbers listed here contain the definitions or examples of the topic listed. It may be necessary, however, to read text on preceding pages or the pages following to understand the topic fully. Also, on some page numbers listed here you will find "good examples" of the topic, but they may not offer any explanation. It is very important, therefore, for you to be sure you correct and complete your homework and keep it organized. Your record of the problems related to these topics may be your best index to understanding the mathematics of this course.